Craft

Gideon's Way

Cover by Susan Mayer.
Blouse from Dusk.
Ear-rings by Adrien Mann.

ISBN   0-85116-605 9

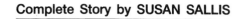
Complete Story by SUSAN SALLIS

An awesome task to ask of a new-born baby . . .

To Bring Together A Family

JENNY lay back among the pillows, watching the life of the busy ward with delightful post-natal lethargy. It was all so different from when she'd had Tom.

For one thing, it was 17 years later; she was 41 instead of 24. For another, this time it was a girl.

There were many other differences, too. Husbands had not been welcome at the bedside when she'd had Tom, and during her labour — in spite of all the attention — she had felt unutterably lonely.

Not that Harry had wanted to watch Tom's birth. He had turned up once everything was tidy and produced a poem he had written, a song of triumph and courage that had borne no resemblance to the hours of sheer toil when the only voices she had heard had been saying either "Relax, dear," or "Push a little harder, dear."

This time, George had been here with her. His gentle voice had kept telling her how well she was doing, how wonderful she was, how very much he loved her. He'd been reassuring.

And at the actual moment of birth he had put his face close to hers, his eyes shining, and he had whispered, "Darling — Elizabeth is here — you've done it . . . Elizabeth has arrived!"

Not "It's a girl." But "Elizabeth has arrived."

She had smiled back at him, the miraculous peace of birth upon her.

"George, I love you," she whispered.

Very suddenly, his eyes had overflowed. He had picked up her hands and covered his face with them and she could feel him pressing her palms hard against his cheeks. She had told him before that she loved him, but perhaps he had felt Harry's invisible presence between them.

He arrived with flowers the next day. In an unmasculine shopping bag he had grapes, fruit juice, chocolates, cheese biscuits — in case she "felt peckish" in the night — and a teething ring for Elizabeth.

Jenny laughed helplessly, deeply touched, because she knew why he had brought so much. Tom was not going to visit her.

She said, "Of course I'm fine. And Elizabeth is fine. Just because I'm an old mum — "

"Forty's not old! Life begins at forty!"

It was the sort of thing he was always saying in front of Tom, and which annoyed Tom unbearably.

Jenny shook her head at him.

"You're always lopping a year off my age. I'm forty-one."

"You're marvellous, that's all I know."

"You're marvellouser than me!" She giggled, glad such a silly thing could bring that light into George's eyes.

She was very sensible in front of Tom. Every time George paid her one of his compliments, she felt it annoy Tom, and she played it right down.

Now she could hold George's hand and thank him for staying with her. They could hang over the cot and admire Elizabeth. They could relax.

BEFORE he went she managed to ask him obliquely about Tom.

"Is he pulling his weight? Making his bed? Washing up?"

'Of course!" George said bluffly, so that she knew he was lying.

"Tell him to pop in to see me on his half day." Tom was at the sixth-form college, and Wednesday was Games afternoon, which he always skipped.

"I did mention it. He's playing in the match against Felburn, I think he said."

She avoided looking at George. It was terribly important to her to keep up the pretence that Tom accepted his stepfather.

"Wish him luck from me then," she said. "Tell him I'm fine."

"I will."

Dear George. He would. He would keep telling Tom how well she was, and how wonderful she was, and it would get on Tom's nerves.

George was almost too nice. He never lost his temper as Harry had done, he didn't whisk them out to dinner when she had prepared it at home. He didn't write poetry.

Tom thought he was dull.

She sighed, and George, misinterpreting, said, "This must be a sad time as well as a happy one for you, Jen. It must make you think of when you had Tom . . . "

She wished she could explain how it was. Harry had filled her life in a way that George didn't, yet George was . . . there. Even when he was at the office, she was conscious of his love and support in a way she had never been with Harry.

She shook her head, baffled. She rarely mentioned Harry, certain that his very name hurt George. Now she said smilingly, "Actually he wasn't here at all. I was remembering that just now. I think if Harry had stayed he might have passed out."

It was meant to be funny, and George smiled obediently. "Of course, he was a poet. Sensitive. Tom has told me."

Jenny remembered wryly the times when Harry, sensitive or not, had trounced Tom soundly across the seat of his trousers.

"Tom has a lot of illusions about his father — he thinks they're memories." She pressed his hand. "Feed-time coming up, darling. Will you be in tomorrow?"

"Try to keep me away!" He grinned at her, and she wondered what she had done to deserve such love. "Anything you want?"

She smiled around at the array of gifts he had already brought, and said without thinking, "Only Tom."

She added immediately, "And he'd make the place look untidy, so it's just as well he's playing football."

George said nothing. His eyes kept smiling, and his kiss was warm.

Propped against the bed-rest, feeding Elizabeth and marvelling at the perfection of her, she knew that the only way of ensuring that George was not hurt was for Tom to live away from home.

Tom had said nothing about leaving home, although it was obvious George got on his nerves. And since he'd known his mother was pregnant, his antagonism had been only just beneath the surface.

Very gently she touched her lips to her daughter's downy head. It was as if she was having to choose between her children. And she loved them both.

A TEAR rolled down her cheek and fell on the baby's fore-head, and the nurse bustled to her bedside.

"Now, Mrs Brewster, this won't do! A little bit of depression, is it? Quite natural at this time. But we must remember what a clever girl we are, mustn't we?"

Jenny smiled obediently. How she wished she could share that fatuous reassurance with George and Tom tomorrow, and that they could all laugh together.

Tom had been 10 when Harry died. A very impressionable age, his grandparents had said.

Harry had given up journalism some years before to be a full-time poet, so there had been very little money left for Jenny and Tom.

Jenny had a fairly good job which fitted in with Tom's school hours, and he was happy in the small town by the river.

By the time Tom was ready to start at the sixth-form college, they had a deposit for a flat. Jenny went to the house agents, and was

"It's playtime for Pepe, an apricot toy poodle. "He's a little scamp," Margaret Dixon of Crook says. "Everything is a game to him.""

Mrs Dorothy Peters of Hockwold-cum-Wilton wanted us to see this lovely photograph of Sam and Tandy, with grand-daughter Jessica. "Both dogs had been abandoned when we rescued them."

TO BRING TOGETHER A FAMILY

shown "a selection of properties" by a curiously old-fashioned, courteous man, who blushed a little as he shook her hand.

"George Brewster at your service, Mrs Minton."

Tom called him "Old Brewster" and mimicked him so well that Jenny held her sides with laughter even as she shook her head reprovingly.

"He's so good and kind. You shouldn't make fun of him."

George Brewster found them a flat, which had a view of the river, faced south and was just what they wanted. He helped them to move in and asked if he might call occasionally.

Jenny was surprised to find she felt relieved. She had wondered whether George Brewster's attentions were entirely professional, and she was beginning to realise that life would be much harder without him.

George had soon established himself in their small family. He met their friends, both sets of grandparents; he read Harry's poems and looked at old photographs. Tom still treated him as a joke, and referred to him as "Mum's admirer."

What he didn't see was that the admiration was reciprocated. Jenny had never met anyone like George before. His kindness was based on

A Pet

Keeping an eye on everyone are the delightful Lucy and Daisy. Mrs Fry of Whitstable tells us they are her daughter's cats.

"Who's a pretty boy, then?" Jackie Tugwell of Bristol says that her Burmese cat went exploring in her neighbour's kitchen.

TO BRING TOGETHER A FAMILY

the fact that he quite naturally thought of others before himself.

She did not know whether her feeling was love; it was not the sort of excitement she had felt with Harry. When Harry died, the emptiness had been perpetual agony. If George left she would not feel that.

But even so, she did not want George to leave.

When he'd asked her to marry him, she'd felt again that enormous relief. She would not have to cope without him.

She tried to tell Tom casually, as if she and George were having another evening at the theatre. She was at the sink, her back to him, but she could hear the complete disbelief in his voice.

"Married? What d'you mean, you're going to get married?"

Jenny went on washing up.

"It's not difficult to understand, surely, dear? You know George has been taking me out now and then — "

"George? Old *Brewster*? You can't mean it?"

She turned calmly and reached for the tea cloth. Tom was sitting at the kitchen table, his homework spread around him. He looked so much like Harry had looked at his age, the age she'd first met him — 16.

9

TO BRING TOGETHER A FAMILY

She peeled off her gloves and hung them over the tap: of course Tom looked like his father. What did she expect?

"I thought you liked George?"

Tom ran an impatient hand through his dark hair. "I do. He's all right. But you can't marry him, Mum!"

She kept her voice as calm as her movements as she began to dry their supper dishes.

"Why not? We get on extremely well. He's a lonely bachelor, and I'm a widow — "

"You're not lonely! I'm here."

She said nothing at all. After she had dried another two plates he added sheepishly, "Well, I didn't know you were lonely, did I? I can stay in, if it's like that. You can't marry George just for companionship, Mum!"

"Why not?" she asked again, remembering Harry at 16 — impulsive, full of dreams, vital, the life in him like a vivid spark.

George wasn't like that. He was there, placid, steady. His life spark glowed comfortably.

"You just can't. It's too feeble!"

She had to laugh at that, but she knew what he meant.

"I'm forty, dear, and no beauty. Why else should I marry?"

He didn't argue. She could see him thinking around it, beginning to accept it. George could never replace his father, but as a companion . . . She was doubtful again. Was that why she was marrying George?

"You still don't have to marry him, Mum," Tom argued. "We could go out together now and then. The cinema. Things like that."

She forced a laugh. "Oh, yes. And to one of the discos at college perhaps?"

Tom looked embarrassed, as if he thought she might be serious.

"I suppose if it's just for companionship . . . " he said tamely.

Jenny had gone on wondering whether her memories of Harry would come between them. But on their wedding night her feelings for George changed.

All she knew for certain was that she loved him with the same intensity. She was a young girl again. Nothing had changed.

Then on her forty-first birthday, she knew she was pregnant. George was so happy it hurt to see him.

"Darling, are you absolutely sure? I wouldn't want you to be disappointed."

There had been no question of how much he would be disappointed.

"I am sure, George. I've been to the doctor's — had a test — it will be in May. The end of May."

"Oh, Jenny . . . you've given me so much happiness, my dear. And now this!"

She smiled tremulously. "It's the other way round — "

He put a finger to her lips. "No. You don't have to say that, Jen. I understand."

Tom had come in then, before she could tell George that he didn't understand at all — and neither did she.

George had been ready to tell Tom the news, but Jenny put her hand on his to restrain him. Later, she'd told Tom privately.

And when she'd broken the news, Tom's reaction had been predictable.

"Oh no, Mum! I'll be the laughing stock of the college!"

Jenny tightened her hands in her lap.

"I don't see why. There might even be some of your friends who will envy you."

He wouldn't meet her eyes. She could see he was hurt, but it was time he began to grow up.

"Look, we are married — and George — "

"All right! You don't have to explain."

She was powerless against the pain in his voice.

"I can't force you to like the idea of the baby," she began. "But please keep your feelings to yourself. George is so happy — "

"I bet he is!" Tom flung at her bitterly, and they had both known instantly that those words were unforgivable.

Since then he had let his indifference to George show, and ignored his mother almost completely. He would be happier away from them.

Jenny wondered why he hadn't gone before . . .

S HE was expecting no visitors on Wednesday afternoon. George would be working, and Tom "playing football". Her own parents were not coming down till the end of the week.

So it was a shock to see the swing doors open, and Tom enter the ward. And then she saw that behind him — very close behind him — came George.

She remembered George asking her if there was anything she wanted; she remembered her reply: "Only Tom," and her heart sank. If George had forced him here, the breach between them would be open for good.

Tom kissed her on the cheek. His eyes were stony cold.

"Hello, Mum. Glad it all went well. George told me you were OK, so I didn't bother — "

"Of course — no need." She spoke as awkwardly as he did, patting the bed, drawing up her knees to make room for him.

"I'll get chairs," George said levelly. Before he left, he looked at Tom just once. *Continued on page 14.*

THERE must be something of a hoarder in us all, but I think my ration of the squirrel instinct was an abundant one.

It all started with a jumble sale to swell our playgroup funds. The things people throw out! I actually ended up bringing home more than I had contributed!

However, it's no good just *going* to jumble sales. Let the word go round that you are available to clean things up afterwards. That's when I spot all my kind of goodies.

Now I may not be an expert on every subject, but I can lay my hands on plenty of knowledge. If you want to take up meditation or rear ducks or camp in the Arctic Circle or try your hand at Russian cookery, come to me first as I'm sure to have a book about it. Well, it was such a shame to see all those good books begging for a home.

There are enough sacks of material in my attic to make at least 50 patchwork quilts and thousands of lavender bags. The snag is, I don't sew much. However, come a fancy-dress competition, and I'm in my element.

Youngsters of all shapes and sizes come knocking on my door, saying, "Please, Mummy wants to know if you've something for a clown costume or a scarecrow or a bunny girl." And I usually have.

In different colour-graded bags lurk pounds of wool, unravelled from numerous sweaters. Unfortunately, I don't knit much.

Still, my youngest daughter is the envy of her friends. When woollen pom-pom making was the rage, she worked up quite a lucrative little business. She had every colour you could think of, and she would charge one sweet for an ordinary

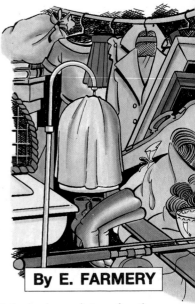

I admit it — I'm hooked on jumble sales. I can always see a use for what other people have thrown out (with the result that I always bring home more than I gave!)

By E. FARMERY

dull shade and two for the more subtle hues.

As for that elusive button — take your choice from about six tins. There are buckles and beads, too.

Clothing is a bit different. Now I don't mind having five pairs of fur-lined boots — all a bit out of date, it's true, but frozen feet never complain.

Our chickens don't turn a feather when I feed them dressed in scarlet slacks and orange anorak! The children grow suspicious, however, and start asking, "Where did you buy it?"

They object to wearing "Joan down the road's last year's coat" in case she recognises it. I obviously

Every One A Gem

had to think along new lines and that's when "Auntie Minnie" came to life.

AUNTIE MINNIE, let me explain, lives a long, long way from here and has lots of grandchildren who grow out of their lovely clothes so quickly that Auntie Minnie, being a very thoughtful, kind and thrifty person, sends them to us!

"No, that wasn't your skirt," protested daughter Kate one day, clutching her favourite flowery cast-off away from a thoughtless child. "My Auntie Minnie sent it."

"Auntie Minnie" is now the family password! Even if I do wear something new it usually gets a casual glance and a remark of "Auntie Minnie been clearing out again?"

The word must be really getting around, though. A perfect stranger knocked on my door the other day and asked if I'd such a thing as an empty violin case. Oddly enough, I had — stored in the attic alongside a baby bath, a cat basket, a bird cage and an odd ski.

It was like tackling a commando course to reach it. I'd to climb over the pile of picture frames (for when I start doing flower pictures); in and out of the 20 odd vases (for when I find time to do flower arranging); through the maze of string and cord (in case I want to tackle macrame at any time); under the bunches of dried flowers and herbs, past the fishing rods and riding boots — the far corner of the attic seemed miles away.

I'd rescued the violin case on the off-chance that one of the children might want to take up the violin — that way we'd only have to buy the violin . . .

However, none of my offspring has a musical talent and I handed over the case with pleasure. It gives me great satisfaction to fill a gap for other people.

My only prayer to the saint who looks after the interest of addicts like me is — don't let the mice get to know. Then, one day, when I'm gone, my grandchildren can have a glorious, requiem jumble sale of their own. □

TO BRING TOGETHER A FAMILY

Continued from page 11.

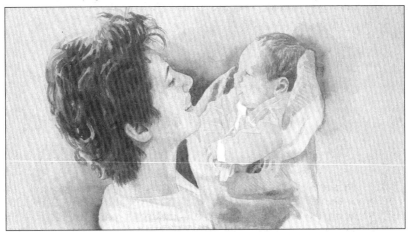

While George went into the corridor for chairs, Tom told her that college was fine, they were having good meals, the flat was fairly tidy.

Jenny was not deceived. She thought painfully that it had been almost better to be ignored than to be treated with this enforced politeness.

George returned and placed the chairs carefully. He beamed at them both. "Well, now . . . where's the young lady we've really come to see?"

Tom lowered his dark eyes to the bedspread and was silent. Jenny felt she could not bear it. Elizabeth was so vulnerable, so innocent.

The nurse wheeled in the cot, and George hovered proudly. Elizabeth was asleep with her arms upflung.

For the first time Jenny saw that she was not beautiful. She was plain and she had a rash across her forehead. Jenny wanted to cradle her, hold her against the whole world.

"Look at her hair, Tom," George observed. "It's going to be black, don't you think? And her eyes are blue now but they're obviously going to darken. And look at those ears!"

He hung over the crib, and Tom came reluctantly to join him.

Elizabeth opened her eyes. Her head moved; first to one side, then the other. She thought it was tea-time.

Tom watched her. As he watched, her face collapsed, her eyes screwed into pinpoints and she began to cry.

"Joggle her, Tom." George moved back. "Go on, just joggle her a bit. It's not time for her feed yet."

Tom joggled half-heartedly. The crying was reduced to some unlady-like grunts, and he joggled some more.

"She's — she reminds me of — me," he said, a note of disbelief in his voice.

14

"Of course she does!" George said. "She's your sister!"

Tom looked up sharply. George was watching the baby, it appeared. "We're a family."

It was so natural, the way George said it. Yet both Jenny and Tom looked at him as if he had made a revelation.

"But I'm supposed to look like Dad," Tom said.

"I've thought so often when I looked through your photograph album," George agreed. "It'll be nice — later — for Elizabeth to know what *her* stepfather looked like."

TOM stared at him for a long moment, then back into the crib. "Of course. Dad would be her stepfather, just as . . ."

"Exactly. And now you've got that straight, let me tell you one more thing." George's voice was still level, but he had flushed.

"I've never tried to take your father's place, Tom. The Tom who is my stepson and the Jenny who is my wife are the people that Harry Minton made them. That is why I love them."

Tom was still too young to take that word. Love. He looked down into the cot again and joggled experimentally.

"You can take that, or leave it," George said with finality. "But you're going to have to come to terms with it somehow. That's all."

He stared at Tom for a moment, then turned and walked out of the ward.

Stunned, Jenny looked across at her son and daughter. Tom was staring after George, forgetting to joggle, and Elizabeth began once again to cry.

He looked into the crib and said uncertainly, "Mum . . . "

"Push her a bit closer, love," Jenny said, and hushed her daughter abstractedly as she watched Tom almost run to the ward door.

She understood, now — understood her own feelings at last. Harry was part of her, part of Tom. And all that she was, loved George . . .

They were coming back now, not looking at each other, shy. Tom made straight for the crib, and Jenny stretched out her hand to her husband.

"I love you, George Brewster," she said.

The nurse came up with clean cot sheets.

"Going to your big brother, are you?" she cooed to Elizabeth. "While you get a nice clean bed?"

And Tom was cradling her, automatically if inexpertly, just as Harry had cradled him 17 years ago.

"A brand new sister for you, dear," the nurse said. "Isn't that nice?"

Tom looked up, surprise written all over his face. "Yes. Yes, it is."

Jenny, still holding George's hand, squeezed it gently. Happiness fluttered inside her and settled down to make a permanent place in her heart. □

BE MY Valentine

It was a declaration of love so unusual that it set the whole town talking.

MISS LESLEY LINDSAY was marching her class of third-year pupils over to the annexe for their double art period when she saw it. She couldn't miss it. Not unless she'd been completely blind — and completely deaf.

Her whole class, who weren't in the least bit blind, collapsed into an uproar, whispering and clutching at each other, staring at Lesley with delighted horror.

The large advertising hoarding which faced Blairhall School annexe, and which until today had extolled the virtues of a well-known lager, now carried a straight-forward, high-impact sign.

The message was in huge pink letters, adorned liberally with sugar-pink hearts.

I love you, Miss Lindsay, with all my heart.

Embarrassment and panic washed over Lesley, making her feel

B

suddenly weak at the knees. But she heard herself say briskly, "Come along, Three B, *please!*"

She held open the door and watched them stagger past her. They were obviously waiting for some sort of reaction from her.

But there was none. Nothing in her teacher's training had equipped her to pass off this incident. So she retreated behind a mask of inscrutability and set the class to work.

And all the while she seethed!

How could he! Couldn't he just imagine what a class of fourteen-year-old girls would make of it? And it must be all round the school. How could she face the staff, let alone the pupils! Even Tim, her best friend among the staff, would have something to say.

Geoff! Geoff! When will you ever learn, she thought, stacking the freshly-cut paper. Or when would she . . . Because wasn't it just like Geoff to do something like this?

She sat for a moment, a small, slim, smartly-dressed figure. Twenty-three years old and suddenly feeling as if she just couldn't cope any more. Not with her class, and more importantly, not with Geoff.

She had fallen in love with Geoff almost at first sight when they'd met during his last year at art college. Geoff, who sent her flowers to remind her of their little "anniversaries", like that first day they walked in the park and talked and talked, so much that they both missed classes.

Geoff, who lurched through life in a crazy, careless way that had always frightened her, yet attracted her at the same time.

She stood up, smoothed down her skirt, and prepared to face her class.

She ought to have been on her guard this morning, of course, when he'd rung her a full half-hour before her little bedside alarm had been set to ring.

"Hi!"

"Geoff? Is that you?"

"Who else would call you at this time?" he'd said cheerfully.

She'd propped herself on one elbow, peered at the clock and nodded. "Who else?"

"Keep your eyes peeled this morning on the way to the annexe, my love."

"The annexe — Geoff?"

But he'd already rung off.

Too sleepy to work it out, she'd simply shrugged it off for the present. But she shouldn't have. Knowing Geoff, she should have been on guard.

How many times before had Geoff's impulsive gestures left her floundering?

She walked round the class, commenting on work, helping out here and there.

But, inside, Lesley was still knotted up with anger and resentment at this latest prank.

The first week she'd met Geoff, he'd walked her home from a late party. When her party hat had blown into the river, Geoff had plucked off his shoes with great style and had jumped in after it.

She'd been enchanted. But by then she was already more than half in love with him. It didn't seem to matter at the time that he'd caught a dreadful cold afterwards, or that he'd passed it on to her and she'd missed an important exam.

Then, on her twentieth birthday, he'd kissed her warmly.

"Close your eyes," he'd instructed, "and hold out your arms — "

She'd stood there, not knowing what was going on. Then something warm and furry had been put into her arms. A small, plump puppy with a pink tongue and a wiggly, brown tail.

Benjamin had been such an adorable little creature and at the time she'd been so pleased.

Perhaps Geoff hadn't known that he would grow so huge, that he'd eat so much or that she'd end up having to employ a dog-sitter while she went to work because otherwise he'd create havoc.

Benjamin, much as she loved the adorable brute, was a liability.

Geoff himself was a liability. But she loved him. And when he'd bought her the tiny solitaire engagement ring, she'd cried because she was so happy. How could she help loving someone like Geoff? So kind, so generous, so impulsive?

Yet there was something child-like in Geoff's make-up and it was the child in him that worried her.

A T four o'clock she marched over to his digs, her anger still simmering nicely in spite of the steadily-falling snow.

His landlady smiled at her, fondly. Mrs Brownlee liked Geoff, too. But then she was only his landlady. She wasn't planning to marry him!

Geoff opened the door to her, grinning from ear to ear. He was wearing a pair of paint-spattered jeans and what seemed to be several layers of old woolly jumpers. The room was chilly — even colder than outside — and he quickly turned on the gas fire for her.

Lesley's anger evaporated. How typical of Geoff to work here all day in this cold little room and spend money on that silly Valentine billboard instead of feeding the gas meter.

He kissed her, but she stood still, unmoved.

"Well?" He bent his head and stared straight into her eyes. "Did you see it?"

"Did I see it?" She took a step away from him. "How could you have been so stupid, Geoff?" she said. "Can't you just imagine what I went through today — the whispers and giggles — the wisecracks. I won't be allowed to forget this little incident in a hurry!

"Valentine's Day is bad enough when you've got thirty giggling schoolgirls to teach — girls who've got cards and silly verses and 'who fancies who' to think about! Just what kind of authority did I have left today?"

Geoff had turned away from her, away from her attack, and she realised he hadn't thought at all. Not beyond the minute, the gesture. As always.

"It must have cost you a fortune," she exploded.

He was cleaning out brushes at the small sink now.

"What it cost is my business, surely." His voice was quiet. Cool.

Lesley sat down, not even taking her coat off in the chilly little room.

"I didn't dare go into the staff-room. They'll all be talking about it, even Tim!"

He flung the brushes down. "For goodness' sake, Lesley, can you hear yourself? You sound like a prissy little schoolmarm!"

He tried to reach for her. "What's wrong with everyone knowing I love you? It's true. Why shouldn't the whole world know?"

She turned away from him. "Love? If you loved me you'd think about me for a change, instead of going your own sweet way all the time!"

NEITHER of them had ever been slow to anger. They'd had rows before. Rows that had exploded violently and quickly burned themselves out, leaving them quiet and calmed, and usually in each other's arms.

But not this time. This time it was different. This time they were pulling each other apart with every cruel word and this time neither of them would give in.

"And how come," she added finally, "that the cost is your business? I'd have thought it an expense you could ill afford, what with plans for getting married sometime . . . Seems like I'm the only one earning any money at all!"

There! She felt a strange satisfaction when she knew she'd hurt him.

His work meant everything to him, and his landscapes were good. Even Lesley marvelled every time he finished a picture. Marvelled at his talent, his relentless search for perfection . . . But talent was no good without a bit of luck, and so far he hadn't had any.

He stood looking at her, the hurt showing clearly in his eyes.

She longed to go to him, to wrap her arms around him and say she didn't mean it, to kiss and comfort him as she'd done so many times before. But this time they'd gone too far.

"Maybe you just don't ever want to settle down," she said to him at last. "Maybe you never have. You'll never change, Geoff, not in a million years."

"Why should I change? You're the one who ought to change, Lesley. You're the one who's got to realise what life's all about."

He stared into her eyes, and when he spoke again his voice had softened.

"Once I met a girl, and I fell in love. She used to know how to laugh at the world, how to live and love . . ." He touched her cheek lightly with his hand, then stood apart from her.

"You've changed, Lesley, not me. Somewhere, somehow. It's just no good any more, is it?"

She hesitated at the door and looked back. He looked so miserable and yet unreachable.

She didn't cry at all till she got back home.

THE first week she didn't ring him and wasn't surprised at all when he didn't try to see her. They'd reached a watershed. All he needed was time to sort himself out.

The second week, with no word from him, she knew it was serious. The third week she worried herself sick. The fourth week she did her work automatically, dazed by the feeling that she'd lost him.

She dragged herself around, depressed and listless. Even Benjamin caught this mysterious malaise.

If only Geoff would come to her, sweep her into his arms and make everything all right. If only he'd come and give Benjamin that funny whistle, make his tail thump noisily on the floor . . .

But he didn't come. And she grew more and more worried about Benjy's drooping spirits. She felt scared, and so alone. Funny, when she'd always felt Geoff was the one who needed looking after.

Eventually, after two months of existing without him, she swallowed her pride and went round to his digs.

Mrs Brownlee met her on the stairs.

"He's gone to the Lake District. He's got thirty scenes to do for a publisher. He'll be gone a long time. It's a big job, he told me. Worth a lot of money."

Was it Lesley's imagination, or was there an accusing look in those old blue eyes?

"I didn't know," she stammered. And Benjy whimpered and scratched at Geoff's door.

"Well, there it is. He's gone now. I reckon that's that." Mrs Brownlee walked away, shaking her head.

In the end, Benjy had to be dragged forcibly from Geoff's door, and when she got home she wept. Wept because Geoff had gone. Because he'd got his big break at last and she hadn't been there to share it.

Surviving was easier than she'd thought possible. Spring suddenly blossomed into summer without her noticing it.

She still walked to school in the mornings, and walked Benjy in the park at night. She still cooked, ate, slept. And she still missed Geoff with an unbearable ache that was almost an illness.

People were kind to her. Tim Maxwell, her friend in the Geography

BE MY VALENTINE

Department, started taking her out, easing her loneliness.

"We like the same things, you and I," he said to her one evening. "Music. Art. Walking. We're very much alike . . ."

She'd looked away from the warmth she saw in his eyes. They were alike in many ways. She was comfortable with Tim, contented in his company.

He was kind, and he liked her. Somehow that helped, and though she knew she wasn't being fair to Tim, she was so grateful for someone to lean on.

Strangely enough, it was Tim who told her Geoff had come back.

They were sitting in the garden of a country pub. After he'd told her, she'd sipped at her drink and stared into space for a long time before she dared ask. "When?"

"Last week, I think. A cousin of mine knows him well. Mentioned his name." Tim stared into his drink.

"I'm sorry he's come back, Lesley. Do you hate me for saying that?" He smiled and covered her hand with his. "I've enjoyed taking you out, being with you — though I've always suspected that only half of you is with me."

Suddenly, horrifyingly, Lesley felt close to tears. Tim's kindness, his perception, and the shock of suddenly discovering Geoff was back were too much for her.

Tim picked up her jacket and took her hand.

"Come on, let's walk for a bit."

They wandered along by the river in silence for a while till Tim said suddenly, "You still love him."

She turned to him. "Still? Somehow I don't know if that's the right word at all. I loved him, but on my own terms — with all sorts of conditions . . ."

"And now?" he asked her.

She sighed, a long sigh that shuddered through her. "Now I suppose I understand what Geoff meant. Too late, of course," she added, and her voice broke.

Tim put his arms on her shoulders and turned her to look at him. Very gently, he kissed her.

"Never too late, surely? Can it ever be too late when you love someone?"

"But, Tim, you don't understand. After all we said to each other, how we wounded each other . . . Can any love withstand that and still survive?" Her voice had risen to a small, hopeful whisper.

"Find out, Lesley," was all Tim said.

That night, she lay thinking about Geoff, seeing him again, bundled up in those ridiculous woolly sweaters, remembering the way they'd stood on opposite sides of that small, cold room . . .

Geoff, who'd demanded more than she'd felt able to give.

In the morning, before she went to work, she called in at the newspaper offices. On the following Saturday, she sat at home, hardly daring to hope.

Then the phone rang.

"Hello."

"Hello." There was a pause, then she added, "Did you see it?"

She could almost hear the smile in his voice.

"Did I see it — couldn't exactly miss it, could I?" There was another long pause. There was nothing to say — and yet so much. It was hard to know where to begin.

"Lesley — I'll come over." And then he rang off.

Lesley smiled and spread out the local paper in front of her.

There, on the back page, in huge black lettering for the whole world to see, it read:

I love you, Geoff Davis, with all my heart.
                    Lesley Lindsay.

The whole back page was taken up by her message. The cost didn't matter. For who on earth could put a price on being able to say I love you?

When he came, she started to cry because she loved him so much. He took her straight into his arms. It felt like coming home.

She tilted her head up to look at him. He was browner, full of life and vigour — but then hadn't he always been that way? Hadn't Geoff always had a special way of living — a way that she'd been lucky enough to share?

Benjy whimpered and watched them, his tail rhythmically thumping the carpet, head on one side, adoration for Geoff shining out of his round brown eyes.

"Lesley — Lesley," Geoff said, grinning, and hugging her so tight she could hardly breathe. "I can't believe it — what will everyone say?"

"I don't care, Geoff. Why shouldn't the whole world know I love you?"

Then he kissed her for a long, long time.

Geoff's special Valentine to her had long since been pasted over with ads for breakfast cereal and other less romantic things. But in spite of the thousand and one things she had to see to, and the awful rush to get the special licence, Lesley had time to attend to one very important detail.

Just to make sure they never, ever forgot, she instructed the baker to be sure to decorate the wedding cake with small, sugar-pink hearts . . . □

Complete Story by VERONICA CHRISTOPHER

This is
HAROLD

No, not the one in the denim jacket — the other one. You can't see the other one? Well, you're not alone!

W ILLIAM!" I shouted again. For the second time in the space of a few minutes, I went to the kitchen door and surveyed the deserted back garden. My voice rose in exasperation.

"William! If you don't come here at once . . . !" I threatened, then turned to see William skirting the corner of the house slowly, very slowly.

"William," I hissed, "your dinner has been ready for five minutes."

My four-year-old son looked up at me.

"I heard you," he said, hurrying not one step. "We couldn't come any faster. Harold twisted his ankle."

Harold! I thought. It would be!

They came on slowly, painfully. William and his friend. I could but wait.

THIS IS HAROLD

William, my son, is easy to explain. He's a small, brown-haired edition of his father, but with more imagination.

Harold is — well, Harold *isn't*, would be more to the point. He's William's best friend and a figment of his imagination. That isn't to say he doesn't exist. He more than exists in our household; at times he dominates it.

Take the present situation, for instance. I could have descended on my small son, picked him up and carried him to the dinner table. But having done that, there was no way in which I could have forced him to eat, if he didn't want to.

So I waited till William was comfortably seated with Harold beside him.

"What's for dinner?" my son asked.

"Stew and dumplings," I said.

"Harold doesn't like stew and dumplings."

"Then he'll have to do without."

"I don't like it much either," William said.

"Too bad," I sympathised, placing a dish before him. "Eat!"

William eyed the stew, then me, but he began to eat. There are times when even *I* refuse to be intimidated.

William hasn't yet demanded that a place should actually be set for Harold or that he should be fed. But when that day comes, either Harold or I will have to go!

With whispered asides to Harold and reproachful glances at me, William ate the stew.

Ice-cream followed. As it melted in William's mouth, his heart melted towards his mum. He gave me his usual sweet smile and even ignored Harold. I don't know whether Harold likes ice-cream but I noticed he didn't get offered any.

"Mrs Webster next door makes nice biscuits," William remarked.

"Oh," I said. "How do you know?"

"She gave us some."

"When?"

"When we went in to see her new kittens. Did you know Tiddles has new kittens?"

"No."

"Well, he has."

"She has," I corrected.

"They were coconut ones," William told me.

"Coconut kittens?"

"No, silly — biscuits. She told us to take two."

"Nice of her," I said.

William wrinkled his brow. "Do you think she meant two each, or one for Harold and one for me?"

I froze. Two each meant four; four meant one greedy little boy or the explanation of an invisible Harold.

"How many did you take?" I asked quickly.

"Only two," William said, "but do you think — "

"Good boy," I said.

So far Harold hasn't strayed beyond the confines of the family, and I'd like to keep it that way.

"What would you like to do this afternoon?" I asked. "Go into town?" Bearing in mind Harold's bad foot, we'd be leaving him behind.

"On the bus?"

"Yes. Daddy has the car. We might look in on him at the office."

"Oh, yes. Gosh — on the bus!"

I marvelled at the simple joy the prospect of a journey by public transport could bring to the young, so blasé about travelling by car. In my youth it was the other way round.

Ah well, that's progress.

ON our way to the bus stop we had to pass the local infants' school. There was the inevitable ritual of stopping for a few minutes to look through the railings. The children were assembling in the playground for the afternoon session and we watched as a whistle blew and ranks of sturdy tots obeyed its signal to make an orderly crocodile.

"How long now, Mummy?"

I'd heard that particular question many times before.

"One month, two weeks and three days." He wasn't the only one counting.

"One month, two weeks and three days," William repeated.

I knew that his imagination might stretch to the three days — perhaps even to the two weeks, but certainly not the month to his fifth birthday. To a four-year-old, months might as well be years.

"Come on," I said, "or we'll miss the bus."

We didn't. We had five minutes to spare, and when it came it was only half full, so we had our choice of a double seat. William wanted to go on the top deck, but I steered him inside.

As the journey progressed, the bus filled up.

"No standing inside," the conductor called.

A large lady hovered near us, wondering, no doubt, whether she would have to get off or go upstairs.

I felt sympathetic.

"Here," I said to her. Then, to William, "Get up, darling, and let the lady sit down." I scooped him up, sat him on my knee and made room for the large lady.

I don't know whether she thanked me or not, because the next moment nothing was audible but William's scream.

"No," he cried, "you can't!"

To my horror, he tried to push the woman.

"William! Stop that!"

But William didn't stop. "Harold. She's sitting on Harold!"

THIS IS HAROLD

"William, don't be silly."

The woman, her face a picture of horror, half-rose. She looked at the empty seat and sat down again.

"Harold!" William repeated. "Get off Harold!"

By this time the whole of the lower deck was taking an interest in the drama.

"What is it?"

"The little boy — his pet, maybe."

"Can't see."

"A hamster? His pet mouse?"

It was the word "mouse", I think, that scared off the large lady. She shot out of her seat and cowered in the gangway, her eyes darting in every direction.

I shot up, too, clutching a still-wailing William.

The conductor ambled down from the upper deck.

"What's going on?" he asked.

"Next stop, please," I said, and rushed to the platform, praying that the bus would stop soon.

It did, and I dragged William off and started to walk quickly homewards.

We didn't even stop outside the school railings on the way back. I simply walked on as if the school didn't exist, and William obviously sensed that he wasn't on a winning streak.

I T wasn't till William was in bed that evening, and Rick, my husband, and I were sipping coffee after our evening meal that the subject of Harold came up. I told Rick, in detail, about the incident on the bus.

Now, he is as aware as I am of Harold's existence. But not being with William each and every day, he doesn't quite realise the trouble that it can cause. We differ in that he finds the Harold syndrome amusing — and I don't.

So, as I finished my saga, I shouldn't have been surprised to find Rick's chuckle turning into a laugh that didn't stop till the tears were running down his cheeks.

"It wasn't funny!" I shouted.

Rick's face slowly regained his composure. "No, darling, it wouldn't be — not for you."

"*Harold* isn't funny," I said. "I'm worried, really worried."

Rick put an arm round my shoulders.

"Darling, I'm sure you needn't be. It's just that William has a vivid imagination. He hasn't anybody of his own age to play with, so he's invented Harold. It's quite normal. All kids have fantasies and Harold is William's."

We sat in silence for a while.

"Perhaps he's quite a nice little chap," Rick mused.

"Who?"

"Harold."

I threw a cushion at him — and missed.

On my way up to bed, I looked in on William, opening the door softly so as not to disturb him.

I couldn't believe my eyes. The bed was empty, and beside it, on the floor, lay William.

"Rick!"

Rick, half way up the stairs, was in the room in a flash. He passed me and knelt down beside William.

"He must have fallen out of bed," I wailed. "But why didn't we hear him? Oh, Rick."

"If you fall out of bed you don't end up fast asleep in a comfortable position with a nice, warm eiderdown over you." He touched William's cheek.

"Hey, there! William."

William stirred, his eyelids flickered, he smiled and opened his eyes.

"What's all this, eh?" Rick asked. "The bed too soft for you?"

He lifted William, eiderdown and all, and was about to deposit him on the bed.

"No!" William protested. "Not there! Harold's there. His foot was hurting so I said he could sleep in my bed and I'd sleep in his."

I hadn't known Harold slept just there on the floor. I must have stepped on him hundreds of times.

"Very thoughtful of you, son," Rick was saying. "But I'm sure your bed is big enough for you both."

"Well — " William looked thoughtfully at the width of the pillow. "Maybe, if I keep to the edge."

"I'll tuck you in so you don't fall out," Rick said, and William smiled up at him gratefully. "Hope Harold feels better in the morning."

THREE days later, the letter came. It was brought round by hand from the school to say that, as there were a few vacancies, they were asking if any children eligible for admission on their fifth birthday would like to attend shortly before that date. William could start the following week.

I told William at once, and we joined hands and did a little dance round the kitchen. I don't know which of us was happier. It wasn't till later that I began to wonder what *I* had to celebrate.

William had filled my life for nearly five years. Now he was going out into the world on his own and I was going to be lonely. I even shed a few tears before realising that every mother whose child went through those school gates must have felt this way, too.

As I put on my coat, having made sure William was clean, neat and fully prepared for what his first morning at school would bring, he asked, "Where are you going, Mummy?"

"With you, of course." I smiled. "To school."

"I can go on my own." He sounded stubborn.

"William," I said, "if you think I'm going to let you cross that road by yourself, you'd better think again."

"There's a lollipop lady." William doesn't miss a thing.

"Today," I told him, "I'm your lollipop lady. Come on."

He walked a few steps ahead of me, his hands firmly in his pockets. At the school gate, he turned and gave me that angelic smile that means all's well with his world.

"Goodbye, Mummy," he said.

"Darling, I must come in with you — this first time, anyway, to tell them who you are and where you live."

"I know who I am and where I live," he said.

I couldn't dispute that, and this time, because I didn't want to upset him, I let him win.

"All right, darling. See you at lunchtime." I bent down and he honoured me with a kiss.

"Goodbye, Mummy," he said, turning at the gate. "Come on, Harold."

Harold! Oh, no! I wondered how his teacher was going to deal with that phenomenon. I went slowly home and worried all morning.

At lunchtime William came bounding out of the school entrance with the rest of the children, looking cheerful and relaxed. He chattered happily all the way home and even forgot not to hold my hand.

"So," I commented, as I dished up the dinner, "you like school?"

He looked at me as if it was a silly question. "Yes." Then, his face becoming serious and his voice dropping, he went on, "But Harold doesn't. He doesn't want to go back. Does he have to go back, Mummy?"

"I don't suppose he'd be missed if he didn't," I said drily.

William brightened. "Oh, good. So he can stay here with you. Keep you company."

"Thank you," I said.

Rick was amused when I told him.

"You'll see," he answered me. "This Harold business will disappear in no time now he's got real kids to play with."

But Harold didn't disappear and when William was at school, I found myself suddenly remembering Harold and feeling guilty that I wasn't taking much notice of him. But I never knew just where he was, this unseen presence that followed me around.

As the days went by, of course, there were Davids and Johns and Tonys sprinkling William's conversation. It was a good sign.

Then William was invited to a birthday party. It promised to be the first of many, with a number of four-year-olds coming up to five.

"Mum," he said when he came back from the party, "can I have a party on my birthday?"

"Of course, darling." William always did anyway.

"With real boys?"

I thought of previous celebrations with grandparents, aunties and uncles.

"With real boys," I promised him.

Having convinced William that his inadequate mum could not cope with his entire class, we tried to limit the number of invitations to ten.

The guests changed from day to day, till in desperation I made out ten small cards with the time, place and occasion written on them and left it to William to distribute them. When he came home, he appeared to have asked two Johns, a Peter, a Tony, three Davids, Andrew, Thomas — and Harold.

I omitted to mention that we needn't have wasted a card on Harold. We could merely have asked him. But I consoled myself with the fact that at least he wouldn't make much noise.

One by one, the boys began to arrive on the day of the party — each accompanied by his mother. By this time I knew most of the mothers. We had met often outside the school gate.

However, one of them was a stranger to me. She was small, neat, with a cheery smile and merry dark eyes that bore no resemblance to the solemn ones of the sandy-haired little boy beside her.

"Hello," she said. "I'm Mary Timson. I've brought Harold."

I looked at the passive, little face beside her and I smiled. I put my hand out to him.

"Oh, William has another friend called Harold," I said.

Then William appeared, and Harold's face broke into a grin.

"William," I said, "you didn't tell me you knew another boy called Harold."

His eyes swivelled from Harold to me. Their look was blank, uncomprehending. After a moment he said, patiently, as if explaining the obvious, "*This* is my friend Harold."

And that, quite simply, was that!

The day I'd longed for, prayed for, had finally arrived. Harold — *our* Harold — disappeared into the air from whence he came.

I know I ought to be relieved. But sometimes I get the feeling that he's still around, unseen, ignored, wistfully watching as I go about the daily round — and — I can't help it — I feel quite sad. □

SPRING comes slowly to the Highlands, especially when the March winds blow in from the North-East. Blinding blizzards of snow can smother the snowdrops and send the multi-coloured crocuses cowering back into their bulbs.

The peeking primroses cover their faces with their green frond-like hands, while the daffodils, not easily deceived and always fearful of March and April, steadfastly refuse to open their buds until assured of a long, loving kiss from the sun.

The birds take a different view, especially the missel thrush. He isn't called the "storm cock" for nothing, as he sings defiantly into the teeth of the blizzard. His message to all the other birds is that the time has come to find a mate, make a home, and rear a family.

The ravens were the first to answer his call, circling the peak of Creag Mhor to claim this nesting place as their own. They didn't even have to take the trouble to make a nest. There was an eyrie there, built by a pair of golden eagles and deserted.

This was a bonus for the ravens who only had to weave a blanket of sheep's wool through the frame of carefully-constructed silver birch boughs.

RORY
My Friend Of The Air

Every time I see a raven flying bold and free, I wonder if it's Rory — and if he remembers when he was one of our family.

All went smoothly with the ravens' romance until one morning in May. The peace of the Creag Mhor peak was shattered with their raucous croaks as they took turns to battle with a big buzzard that flew overhead.

The buzzard had only one thing in mind. It lowered its head and looked down its cruel, curved beak to gaze, with glowing golden eyes, at the young raven that had tumbled out of the nest and now lay sprawled on a ledge far below.

As I watched, the buzzard brushed aside the ravens' aerial attack and flexed its talons. Any moment now it would dive down and pick up the young bird.

Yelling at the top of my voice, I raced towards the rocks and clawed my way up the cliff face. The buzzard uttered a shrieking, cat-like mew and with a wave of its massive wingspan, veered away.

I reached the young raven. Having stuffed the squawking bundle of black feathers into my game bag, I made a perilous attempt to climb the rest of the way to the ravens' nest. But there was no way I could surmount or circumvent its craggy overhang of rock, which appeared specially designed to prevent predators from approaching the nest.

The buzzard had gone now. Should I leave the young one on the ledge I had reached? The parent birds circled above me like two black brushes painting their anxiety in the sky.

I knew they would feed and care for the young raven but it would not have the security of the nest. The buzzard would return, or a wild cat or a fox.

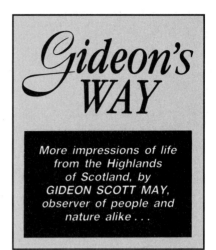

Gideon's WAY

More impressions of life from the Highlands of Scotland, by *GIDEON SCOTT MAY*, observer of people and nature alike . . .

Then my mind was made up for me. The young raven in the nest peeped over the edge and let out a penetrating scream which was answered from my bag with a muffled croak. The parents, in a meaningful dive, almost swept me from my perch.

That settled it. I retired as hastily as I could and the young raven, christened Rory, was installed in the stable at Croft Douglas.

FEEDING him was quite a problem at first. He totally ignored the tasty pieces of chopped liver I placed temptingly in front of him. I tried prising open his beak to slip in a piece of meat but to no avail. Rory just spat it out and sat back, blinking stupidly.

Next, I tried the natural approach and treated him to some full-blooded, deep-throated croaks. Rory's reactions were immediate! He jumped up and down, screeching excitedly, and I found myself staring

C

down his ample gullet. Quickly I popped a piece of liver in.

I repeated this procedure half a dozen times, then, at last, Rory squatted down on the manger, blinking contentedly.

The young raven grew rapidly and had a finger, or rather a feather, in everything that went on around Croft Douglas.

He supervised the feeding of the hens and the milking of the house cow and would try to beat the cat in a wild race for the saucerful of milk. It was usually a dead heat and they sipped, one on either side, and swore at each other.

Rory was a fantastic mimic. He would mew softly and call the kittens — then chuckle in delight at their bewilderment. He could cluck with the laying hens, copy the crowing of the cock and bark like a dog.

I felt sure that, with a little coaxing, I could get him to talk, so each time I fed him I said slowly, "Rory likes liver."

One morning, Rory looked straight at me over his empty plate and in a growly voice, drawn deep down from his breast feathers, said, "Rory likes liver."

Tarra, the collie, and Rory became great friends. Together they herded everything — chickens, kittens and ducklings. But when Tarra was called upon to round up some sheep, Rory was hard put to it to keep up and hopped, flapped, and croaked in despair, until forced to spread his wings.

To his own and Tarra's astonishment, he floated effortlessly. From that moment he directed all proceedings from the air.

The hens weren't giving their usual supply of eggs. I wondered why, until I spotted Rory shuffling stealthily into the henhouse. I peeped around the door and saw Rory crooning huskily to a setting hen. He tenderly tickled her breast feathers with the point of his beak, then robbed her of the newly-laid eggs.

Using his wings for acceleration, he flapped out of the henhouse, triumphantly carrying his trophy. His surprise at seeing me had to be seen to be believed. He sat back on his tail, hiding his head, and the egg, under his wing!

But Rory fully repaid his egg debt when a dog weasel crept into the farmyard.

A mother hen spotted his stealthy approach and shrieked an alarm call. All her brood immediately sought the shelter of her feathered breast as she prepared to defend herself and her chicks.

Help came from the air. Rory, dropping like a stone, dealt the weasel a stunning blow with his beak, picked him up in his claws and made a laboured take-off.

The weasel recovered consciousness in mid-air and squirming around in Rory's claws, bit him savagely in the chest. Rory squawked in pain, released his grip and the weasel dropped down with a thump on the turf, to slink painfully away.

But Rory was badly wounded. He didn't eat a bite for two days. I feared his wounds were infected so I bathed them with whisky and put a little into some warm milk for him to sip.

He swallowed, blinked rapidly, then whispered hoarsely, "Rory likes liver," and proved it by disposing of a saucerful.

Within a week, Rory was back to his old self. Then the wanderlust claimed him as he foraged farther and farther afield.

ONE day when I saw Rory rise replete from a rabbit carcase he had found, I knew he had acquired the priceless gift of independence.

I tucked him under my arm, marvelling at how much he had grown since we had first met, and set off for Creag Mhor, right back to the old eyrie and nesting place.

I held Rory tightly in my arms as my fingers fondly stroked his every feather into its proper place. I realised how much I loved him and his funny ways.

I had to blink repeatedly to clear the mist from my eyes, but Rory was looking at me, and out-blinking me.

I threw him high in the sky. As he circled and inspected the nest, I quickly disappeared lest he be tempted to follow me back to the croft.

A week later I climbed the Creag again and stopped, when I was only halfway up, to watch a kestrel hawk hovering delicately above me.

Suddenly, it screamed and dived straight down the cliff face, fleeing from the black shape that was hurtling towards me. It was Rory!

He landed a few feet from me, dancing around with delight. With a swoop of his great wings, he rose and circled round and round my head, croaking his pleasure at our meeting.

I didn't trust myself to croak back, or linger, and so possibly weaken the links that now bound him to the wild.

As he tilted a wing to show off his latest flying manoeuvre, I waved a fond farewell and raced away.

Every March, when the ravens return to Creag Mhor to inspect and tidy up their nesting site, they treat us to a great display of aerobatics. There is a large cock bird who can outfly them all and execute perfectly the ravens' speciality, sweeping down in a perfect dive, pulling out to level up, then fold his wings to leisurely roll over.

I like to think this is Rory. □

A FADING DREAM

The old is ousted by the new,
Town planners had their say.
Those luscious, rolling, endless fields
Are fading fast today.

The nooks and crannies where we played
And carved our world of fun
Are now engulfed in concrete tombs.
The damage has been done.

The childish laughter seems so strained,
The echoes make me cry,
For cherished thoughts refuse to live
With blocks that blot the sky.

— S. H. W., Swansea.

Was it a waste — all those years spent caring for others? That was the question she asked herself as she took stock of . . .

A Lifetime Of Loving

THE automatic washing machine drones on, swooshing and swishing. It makes me sleepy. The sun comes through the window and warms me, as I sit waiting for the machine to finish its programme.

I'm being spoilt, having the laundry done without lifting a finger. I think back to the old days when there would be a mangle in most backyards in our street and the women wrung their clothes and gossiped at the same time. There was fierce competition for the whitest line of washing.

On long summer evenings they sat on front door steps, talking. Children climbed the walls because there was a scarcity of trees where I grew up.

Most of the children had skinned knees in summer and chilblains in winter.

I can remember so clearly things that happened when I was a girl. That's a sure sign of getting old. Yet I can't recall what I did yesterday, half the time.

The sun on my face takes me back to another place, another time — to when my mother would have me jumping up and down on

**Complete
Story
by DOREEN DADE**

blankets in a huge wooden tub in our backyard.

I can see her face so vividly. Her light-brown hair all damp from the steam, her pretty grey eyes so full of sun, and laughing as she usually was.

"Don't stop now, our Annie. Keep going. The more you jump, the softer they'll be."

And I'd jump more than ever to please her.

"Can I have a jam doorstep when I've done, Mam?" I'd shout.

"Yes, with gooseberry jam," she'd call from the clothes line.

Sometimes I'd see Mam screw up her face. She'd give a little gasp and stand for a minute by the wall, clutching her side.

I'd run to her, calling: "Mam, what's the matter?"

"Don't fret, girl. I'll be fine in a moment. Now you go in and pop the kettle on. A cup of tea will soon put me right. You see if it doesn't."

It went on putting Mam right for a long time. Till the day I came home from school to find my Aunt Dolly waiting in the tiny kitchen. Her face was white and there were tears in her eyes.

"Oh, there you are, Annie. I've been waiting for you," she said, avoiding my eyes.

"Where's Mam?" I asked.

"She's gone to the infirmary, Annie. They're going to give her an operation. She'll be all right, lass, never fret."

"Is it the pain in her side?" I asked.

Aunt Dolly nodded. "Yes, she never told anyone, you see. It got worse. I'll wait for your dad to come in to tell him. Now let's have a bit of tea together."

The bread and jam tasted like ash in my mouth. When I'd finished, I ran up to the room at the top of the stairs and cried and cried. I sensed my mother would never come home.

WHEN the factory hooter went I waited for my father's boots to come clattering down the street. I put my hands over my ears because I didn't want to hear him shout, "Home, pet!"

He always shouted that to Mam.

I could hear the muffled voices of Aunt Dolly and Father for a long time after. My two brothers came in from the mill. I heard my aunt saying goodnight. I still sat up there, shivering and cold.

"Annie!" I heard my eldest brother say softly. I looked at the door and Billy came in, holding a cup of tea and a piece of bread and jam. Tears ran down my face as I saw it was gooseberry jam.

"Billy, will Mam get better?" I asked through a torrent of tears.

He sighed and sat down on my bed. I adored Billy. I loved both my brothers, but Billy especially.

He took my hand and rubbed it in his big, strong one.

"She's let it go on too long, Annie. Didn't want to make a fuss.

That's our mam. Hey, you're frozen, Annie. Here, lass, drink this tea."

I FELT all grown up, just like that: it was as if I became a woman in that short time.

I never saw Mam again. She died before they could operate on her. My father was heartbroken. A big man like that, he seemed to shrink in front of us.

I left school soon after and stayed home to keep house for Dad, Billy and Jimmy. Aunt Dolly was kind and came in frequently to check on us.

"Well, Annie, you've turned into quite a little housewife," she'd say encouragingly at my efforts. "Your mam would be so proud. You'll make someone a grand wife one day."

When my brother Billy was 20, he married a girl called Alice and they rented a tiny house a few streets away. She was soon expecting her first child. I was thrilled about it. I'd go round there every day to keep her company when I'd done the chores at home.

I was only young, but there was something about Alice's appearance that worried me. I couldn't put a finger on it, but there was something.

As the months passed it was clear she wasn't well. She was always so tired, and when I'd call out to her before I opened the door she'd answer in almost a whisper.

"Come in, Annie, I'm just resting." She'd look up at me with her brown eyes, almost as if she wished I hadn't come, so as she could close them and sleep.

"I've brought some beef tea, Alice. Father likes it the way I make it and there's a bit of potato pie for our Billy's tea."

A wan smile crossed her pale face. Like a faint sun on a rainy day and gone just as fast.

"You're a good lass but I wish you'd get a few good times for a change. Ever since I've known you, Annie, you've been looking out for others. You're a pretty lass and it's high time you had a young man!"

I felt a blush rise to my cheeks.

"Oh, there's plenty of time for me," I replied, not looking at her, busying myself with a duster.

There was a young man, at the Friday evening social I sometimes managed to attend — Arthur Pickering. He was nice and he'd walked me home once or twice after these dances.

One night, under a moon as big as a pumpkin, he'd said shyly, "I think you're real pretty, Annie. All that black curly hair and your grey eyes. Will you walk out with me sometime?"

I'd said yes and one Sunday we'd walked out to the wood on the edge of the town, away from the belching factory chimneys and into the clean, sweet air of the countryside.

"I'm thinking of going to Australia," Arthur had said right out of the blue, as we sat on a stile looking over a meadow full of mustard flowers.

I'd nearly fallen off in surprise. Arthur wasn't known to be the most adventurous of people.

"Why?" was all I was able to say.

"Because I think I could do well there. They say there's work for my trade. Will you come with me, Annie?"

Again I nearly lost my perch. I stared at him. His nice face was perfectly serious; his brown eyes were full of love and the sun lay on his fair head like a halo.

"Now Mother's gone," he said, "there's nothing to hold me here. I'm young and strong. With someone like you I could do anything. Say you'll think about it?"

For the first time in my life I felt bitterness dry my mouth.

I couldn't go with Arthur. There was no need to think about it. My future was here — with my father, Jimmy, Billy and Alice.

I jumped down from the stile. "Come on, Arthur, take me home. I've Dad's tea to get."

"You won't think about it then?" he asked.

I felt the tears blur my vision. "There's no need. I can't go and that's flat," I said almost crossly.

ARTHUR left a few weeks later, but he pushed a note under the door before he left. It read:

Dear Annie,

I'm off. Wish me luck. I hope to come back one day. If you marry I wish you well, if you don't . . . well, as I said, I hope to come back. I'll not forget you and your sweet face.

Love, Arthur.

My sister-in-law Alice died giving birth to a daughter. Billy named the child Grace and he came back home to live with us.

I assumed the role of mother to his daughter. I didn't mind as I loved her. It just meant I didn't get out at all now.

Grace was two years old when we lost Dad. I was 20 and looked older. It was a strain being housewife, mother and comforter to them all.

"You're looking peaky," Aunt Dolly remarked when she called in for a chat one day.

"I'm a bit tired, that's all," I replied.

"Well, I think you deserve a break, lass. There's a dance at the town hall this Saturday. Why don't you go? I'll sit with young Grace. I know Billy likes to go out for a drink Saturdays," Aunt Dolly said.

I looked in the mirror above the fireplace. My grey eyes had dark rings under them and I was too thin. However, my hair was just as black and still as curly.

I could buy a piece of material in the market and run up a dress. It would do me good to go to the dance and be with people my own age. I did need a change.

"I think I will go, Aunt Dolly," I said.

★   ★   ★   ★

I knew some of the girls who stood by the door chattering away ten to the dozen, when I arrived at the dance hall. They welcomed me, warmly.

"Annie, that's a lovely dress! Doesn't she look nice?"

It was a grand evening. I spent most of the time dancing. When a stranger asked for the last dance, I was feeling happy and tired. He was tall, with dark brown hair and blue eyes.

"You're the bonniest girl here," he whispered in my ear, as we waltzed round the hall.

I felt quite elated. It had been a long time since I'd been paid so many compliments.

He walked me home and I found out he came from the next town. His name was Joe Willis and he worked in a hosiery factory.

"Can I see you again?" Joe asked when we reached my door all too soon. "Will you be coming to the dance next week?"

My earlier elation evaporated. I was Cinderella again.

"I don't think so."

"Why not? You enjoyed it, didn't you?"

I nodded. "Oh, yes, I loved it. I haven't been anywhere for such a long time . . ." My voice fell away as tears began to slide down my face.

"Why, whatever's the matter?"

"Oh, I can't get out much. I look after my niece who's only two. My brother's wife died and I've looked after her ever since . . ."

"Is that all?" He smiled, and I felt a funny sensation go right through me. I felt as if I'd known him ages.

"Isn't that enough?" I replied, forcing a smile back.

"You really are the prettiest girl, Annie. I'll come and sit with you then. I don't need to go dancing." *Continued on page 43.*

AUTUMN

Autumn
is a hillside dressed in purple
With heather reaching up to touch the sky,
Where we can sit and meditate in silence
And let life's pandemonium pass us by.

Autumn
is a glorious golden cornfield
With scarlet-headed poppies here and there.
Their loveliness is ours for the asking
If only we have time to stand and stare.

Autumn
is a deck-chair in the garden
With vibrant bedding plants in bright array.
The scents of all their blossoms intermingled
Will lend enchantment to a perfect day.

Autumn
is a picnic by the river
With lots of food to eat and games to play,
And then a shady spot beneath an oak tree
To fall asleep and dream our cares away.

Autumn
is the summer softly fading
As mellow mists hang heavy overhead.
The swallows start to congregate together
And green leaves turn to russet, then to red.

Autumn
holds its arms out towards winter
As hours of sunshine slowly disappear
The shadows lengthen and the nights grow cooler
And Autumn drifts away until next year.

— P. C., Southport.

"That wouldn't be fair to you, though," I answered, feeling a warm glow all over. "You'll never meet anyone."

"Perhaps there's no need now," Joe whispered softly.

He said he'd call the next Saturday and I listened to him whistle all the way down the narrow street.

Aunt Dolly smiled at me when I opened the parlour door.

"Well then, our Annie, you look as if you've had a real good time."

"Oh, it was lovely, Aunt Dolly."

"You're going again?" she asked, shrewd eyes boring into me.

"Oh, I can't . . . there's Grace."

"Now, don't be daft. I can easily sit in with her. She's no bother. I bet you danced every dance, didn't you?" She smiled.

"Yes, I did. Actually, I met a very nice lad. He walked me home. He's called Joe — Joe Willis. He had to walk right back to the next town. Imagine," I told her as we sipped our cocoa.

"Well, he must be keen then!" She laughed.

"Oh, Aunt Dolly!" I felt myself blushing.

"Well, five miles is five miles. Are you seeing him again?"

"I said I wouldn't be able to go dancing. I told him about Grace. He said he'd come and keep me company," I replied, feeling that warm glow inside again.

"I told you he was keen!" Aunt Dolly laughed as she set off back to her own house.

SO began our courtship. Every other Saturday Aunt Dolly would sit with Grace while Joe took me dancing.

One night Billy said to me:

"Well, our Annie, you'll be thinking of setting up house for yourself soon. I don't want you to think I expect you to give up your life for us. We'll manage something. I'm real taken with your Joe. He thinks the world of you, too, that's plain to see."

"I'll never leave this house while I'm needed, Billy," I told him earnestly. "As long as Grace needs a mother I'll not desert you and her."

He took my hand.

"You're a good lass, but we'll not stand in the way of your happiness . . ." He paused and looked at the wall behind me. I felt there was something else he wanted to say — I could read it in his face.

"Is there something you'd like to tell me, Billy?" I asked gently.

A smile crossed his pleasant face. "Well, Annie, there is something. I'm not sure I should speak of it yet, but . . ."

"If I can help," I offered.

"Well, there's this lass called Lucy — my age, she is — a widow, with a son. I like her very much. I've taken her walking once or twice and I wondered if I could fetch her home. Maybe you'd like to meet her sometime . . ."

I squeezed his hand. "Oh, of course I would, Billy. I've been worried about you. You're so young and it wouldn't be fair for you to spend the rest of your life on your own."

"It would depend on how Grace takes to her," he said firmly.

"Billy, if you like her, Grace will. Grace likes most folk. You say Lucy has got a son?"

"Yes, little Sammy. He lost his dad down the pit two years back. Lucy's been very lonely. Well, shall I ask them to tea?"

"Yes. How about next Sunday?" I suggested, and he agreed.

I liked Lucy at once and it was clear she doted on Billy. Her little boy and Grace hit it off from the start.

Later, as Lucy helped me wash the pots, she said shyly, "You've made this house a real home. Billy's always telling me how good you've been this last few years."

"Well, it had to be done. Do you think you and Billy will get married?" I asked, and could have bitten my tongue.

Lucy blushed crimson.

"Oh, we've not got around to that yet." She was embarrassed. "I do like him, though, and little Grace is a pet."

"I should miss her if she went," I said. "Still, if Billy was happy, that's all I'd ask."

THEY did marry, shortly after Joe and I became engaged, and Billy and Grace moved into Lucy's house. Joe and I didn't have a long engagement, there didn't seem much point in waiting, though long engagements were the thing in those days.

Three months later we were married and Joe moved in with me. My brother Jimmy still lived in the house as well. He liked Joe so there was no friction.

It was three years before our daughter arrived. I lay exhausted afterwards, looking at the tiny scrap of humanity in my arms. We named her Josephine.

She was the light of our lives and she was never any trouble — a good-natured baby, Josephine had my black hair and her father's blue eyes. As she grew, she and Grace became firm friends. She was always round at Billy's house and Grace round at ours.

She wasn't yet at school when the Second World War broke out.

My darling Joe had to go. There was nothing I could do to keep him. He went like all the others.

As I clung to him on that bleak, blacked-out station, the coldest sensation went right through me.

"Oh, Joe, you'll come back? You'll not desert us?" I cried from my heart.

He held me in his strong arms. They couldn't warm me that time, though. I felt frozen as if I'd never be warm again. His blue eyes were full of sadness but he managed to laugh.

"Desert you, Annie! I'd be daft to do that. Now you just look after yourself and our Josie. I'll be back."

I watched till the train was out of sight. I couldn't weep. I knew I'd never see him again. Don't ask me how I knew . . .

When the news came that Joe had been killed in action, I accepted it calmly. Too calmly. Hadn't I known? Hadn't I known from the start?

Maybe I'd been too happy. In the short time I'd known Joe there hadn't been one unhappy minute. And now he was gone, leaving a terrible void.

Billy went down the mines during the war, as did Jimmy. My brothers and Lucy were a tower of strength to me. In all that time I hadn't cried.

"You should have a good cry, love," Lucy said to me, one afternoon, as we had tea together. "It would get it out of your system."

"I can't cry, Lucy," I told her truthfully. "It's as if my eyes are all dried up. I just can't."

"It's a terrible time you're going through, Annie. I know how you feel. When my Tom went, I just wanted to die. But there was young Sammy. I had to get on with things for his sake. A child's a great blessing. You've Josie to think on now."

I nodded and pressed her hand. "Don't fret, Lucy. I'll get on with things. Later there'll be a time for tears, you'll see."

IN a way, the job at the munitions factory was my salvation. I hadn't time to brood. The work was hard and by the time bedtime came I was too weary to think at all.

I had Josie to bring up as well. She was a lovely girl, but too much like her father for my comfort. His blue eyes looked at me each day through her.

I still cooked for my brother, Jimmy. He'd never been used to mining and came home exhausted every night, with red-rimmed eyes glaring out of a black, dust-lined face.

Oh, yes, I was glad of the hard work then.

The war dragged to its end, and Jimmy and Billy went back to their old jobs in the mill.

A LIFETIME OF LOVING

I took a part-time job in the hosiery factory in the next town.

Josie was growing up into a fine girl. I made her stay on at school for I didn't want her to work in a mill or a factory.

In the end she went to work in the offices of the local shoe factory as a secretary. I was so proud of her.

ONE afternoon as I went about the chores in the house, a young man knocked on the door. I'd seen him walking up the street with a piece of paper in his hand. There was something familiar about his head of fair hair and his deep brown eyes.

"Arthur! Arthur Pickering! You're the living image . . ." I gasped.

He smiled and I was transported back to that summer when Arthur and I had wandered up in the meadows above the chimneys and smoke of the town.

"Miss Braithwaite?" he asked hesitantly.

I took his arm and drew him inside.

"As was, a long time ago." I smiled.

"I'm Arthur's son, Dan. He asked me to look you up. Of course, he didn't know whether you'd left the district . . ."

"I never left, though your father did. Oh, this is a wonderful surprise!"

"Dad's often talked of you. We lost Mum a few years ago. He kept on about the old town where he'd grown up, talked of nothing else when she died. I feel as if I know you, Mrs . . ."

I smiled at him. "Call me Annie. Did he make his fortune then? He was full of high hopes when he left here."

"He did very well. In fact, he's retired now. He says he's coming back soon, though," Dan said.

"It would be lovely to see him again," I said.

"You're on holiday?" I enquired over a cup of tea.

He shook his head. "No, I've come to work — see how I like England. I've got a job through a friend of Dad. From what I've seen so far, I like it a lot."

"Fancy leaving that lovely climate to come to this damp old place!" I laughed.

"Oh, the weather isn't everything. Although I was born over there, I've always felt English. Something seemed to be missing all the time. I can't explain it but when I was walking up this street I felt as if I'd been here before. Can you understand that, Mrs . . . Annie?"

"Yes, dear, I know what you mean. Oh, I can hardly believe this. After all these years — it's like looking at Arthur again," I said, smiling.

Dan was still there when Josie came in from work. I introduced them. Sitting there on the sofa together, fair head near dark one, I had the strangest feeling — that could be me sitting there beside Arthur.

That was the start of their friendship. I wrote and told Arthur, and in his reply to me he wrote:

It seems like Fate that Dan should meet your girl. I always thought the world of you, Annie. No-one ever really took your place. I had a good wife, I'm not saying otherwise, but you were the first love of my life.

I'm glad you had a good marriage, though perhaps too brief. I expect Dan told you I was thinking about coming back to the old country. Truth is, Annie, I don't think I'm up to it, lass. The old heart isn't good.

Deep down I've a feeling it may not be up to a trip home, though I'd give anything to see you again, Annie. I'll have to live on the memories of the way we were, for what time is left to me. I'm grateful for them.

Thanks for the snaps of Josie and all the news. Yes, she is a beauty, but what else would you expect with a mother like she's got?

I really wanted you to come with me, Annie, but it wasn't to be. Now my pleasure is knowing that my Dan and your lass are friendly. It's been a tonic to know that. Look after yourself, Annie. The prettiest girl I ever set eyes on — and that's no lie . . .

The tears I'd dammed up for so long ran down my face as I read that letter. I cried for Arthur, the young lad with such high hopes, I cried for my parents and for my darling Joe.

★　　　★　　　★　　　★

Josie married Dan a couple of years later and I sent the wedding photos to Arthur. He was as delighted as I was.

I'm a grandmother now with two strapping grandsons. They often come to see me in the little house I've lived in for so long. The house that's known so much laughter, tears and love.

I shall stay here for ever. The family have made me very comfortable — with the automatic washing machine, and the television set to entertain me. I count my blessings every day.

It's gone quiet now. The washing machine has finished its programme.

"Gran!" A voice makes me jump. I rise stiffly and open the back door.

"Hello, Joe. Hello, Arthur," I say as they come in, Arthur's fair head followed by Joe's dark one, living replicas of the two men in my life.

"Have you made a cake? We're both starving," Joe asks, his grandad's blue eyes smiling at me.

"I have and I've never known a lad that wasn't starving!"

My two boys sit at the old deal table expectantly.

"Good old Gran," they say.

I sit and watch them eat. Good. It's all as it should be. I've come a full circle and it feels right. □

T HEY took their holiday that year without the children. It was the first time since before Brian was born that they had managed to get away by themselves, and they set out on the trip with all the enthusiasm of their early married days.

Nevertheless, Valerie kept on remembering one more thing she had to tell the children before they left, and yet another safety check she had to make in the house.

Second HONEYMOON

By the time they finally drove away, Peter was laughing at her.

"I just want to be sure we've seen to everything," she said, annoyed at him.

"Seen to everything? I should think you have by now."

"Did you give them enough money for the fortnight?" she asked.

"And some extra."

"Good. I don't want them to go borrowing money from Mum."

"Why not? Your mother loves giving them things."

"That's no reason."

"It's every reason," he joked. "They've been living off us for long enough."

"Hmm," she said.

They had made up their minds. They'd just pack the car and go. And they wouldn't give the children a moment's thought . . .

D

"Look!" he cried, pointing at the sign up ahead. "We are now leaving town. It thanks careful drivers."

"Well, it's got little to thank you for, then."

"Don't nag." He smiled. Nothing was getting past his defences today. "We're about to set off on our first holiday alone together for over eighteen years. No kids, no responsibilities, just me and you and a fortnight all by ourselves. It's about time, too. We deserve a break from constant kid-raising."

The idea of it struck her as quite good, too, now that they were away from the house, from the sight of the children waving goodbye. She relaxed a little and looked at him, concentrating on his driving now.

"We're free," he said.

"We are, aren't we?" She nodded. "Just like the old days."

He laughed.

"What?" she asked, puzzled.

"I was just thinking," he said. "I hope we still get on with each other."

They drove on in a leisurely fashion, stopping for lunch at a pleasant little restaurant on the coast road.

They revelled in the joy of ordering wine, not having to ask for lemonade, eating their favourite delicacies, not suffering the embarrassment of enquiring whether the establishment did egg, beefburgers and chips ("for the children, ha, ha!").

In the afternoon, they left the main road for a quieter country one, taking their time because there were no restless kids in the back.

I T was early evening when they checked in at the hotel where they'd spent their honeymoon. The manager's wife was behind the reception desk. She introduced herself.

Peter started to sign, absentmindedly, as "Peter Morley and family", but Valerie took the pen from him and completed it with just their names. The manager's wife joined in their laughter when they explained.

They settled into their room, then they took a walk up to the cliffs west of the town.

"Lovely!" He took a deep breath of sea air.

"It hasn't changed all that much," she said.

They stood on the cliff top path, looking down to where the town lights were just coming on.

"It hasn't, has it?" He took her hand. "Now then, where are we going to eat tonight?"

They found a restaurant and had a very good meal. It was situated by the beach, and they could see the other side of the bay, the lights twinkling like a necklace as they ate.

When they got back to the hotel, it was all very warm and cosy, and afterwards, in the darkness of the night, they slept.

Or rather, Peter slept. He turned over and was dead to the world in a second.

But Valerie lay on her back, staring at the ceiling, her mind working overtime.

I hope they're all right . . .

I mean, I know they're old enough and sensible enough to look after themselves now, and Brian's in charge . . . but you never know what they get up to . . .

No, if something did go wrong they'd call. They know where we are. They'd call and tell us . . .

Unless, of course, they were trying not to bother us . . .

Vivid images of pipes bursting, the cooker blowing up, lights fusing, the house falling down, flashed through her mind. And in the centre of it all, the children, huddled together in fear, with Brian crying out, "We mustn't disturb them. We don't want to ruin their holiday."

She turned over and cuddled up to Peter's warm body.

Don't be ridiculous, she told herself firmly. They are managing perfectly well at this very moment, and everything is fine.

Yet it was still a long time before she managed to close her eyes and drift into the same oblivion that Peter had managed so easily.

"You look worn out," he remarked next morning at breakfast.

"I'm fine." She managed to smile despite her headache. She stirred her tea gently, so as not to make too much noise. "Just couldn't get off to sleep last night."

"What's up?"

She put a hand up to tuck a strand of fair hair behind her ear. "Nothing."

He studied her carefully. "You're worried about something, aren't you?"

She shook her head.

"Yes, you are. What is it? Not the kids?" He saw the look in her eyes, and nodded to himself. "I thought so."

"Well, I'm not sure it's such a good idea, all this secrecy. All this 'We won't write, we won't phone' business. What if something happens to one of them?"

"They know where we are. In an emergency, we're available."

"But can't we just phone to say hello?"

"If we do that, Anna will start telling you how she's burnt the dinner, and before we know it, you'll be begging to go home and save them. No, we made the rule, and the kids'll stick to it, so why shouldn't we?"

"I just thought . . . "

"That's the trouble." He grinned, buttering a slab of toast as if it were a brick. "You think too much. I know you. You were lying there last night, wide awake, imagining all the horrible things that could have happened to them." *Continued on page 57.*

Materials Required — Of Emu Superwash Double Knit, 3 x 50-gram balls white; 2 x 50-gram balls green; 1 x 50-gram ball each red, yellow and black; one pair each of 3¼ mm, 4 mm and 4½ mm (Nos. 10, 8 and 7) knitting needles; crochet hook; washable toy stuffing; 3 buttons; narrow elastic; black and red felt for face; firm card for hat.

For best results it is essential to use the recommended yarn. If you have difficulty in obtaining the yarn, write direct, enclosing a stamped, addressed envelope, to the following address for stockists: Customer Service, Emu Wools Ltd., Leeds Road, Greengates, Bradford, West Yorkshire BD10 9TE.

Measurement — Height from top of head, 85 centimetres, *33½ inches,* approximately.

Tension — 26 stitches and 34 rows to 10 centimetres, *4 inches,* measured over stocking stitch, using 4 mm needles.

Abbreviations — K — knit; P — purl; st(s) — stitch(es); st-st — stocking-stitch; skpo — slip 1, knit 1, pass slipped stitch over and off needle; tog — together; loop 1 — insert right-hand needle into next stitch as if to knit it, wind yarn round 3 fingers twice, then with yarn still round fingers, wind yarn round needle and draw loop through, place this loop on left-hand needle and knit it together with stitch on needle, let loops fall off fingers; m1 — make a stitch by picking up horizontal loop lying before next stitch and knitting into back of it; **M** — main colour (white); **A** — 1st contrast (green); **B** — 2nd contrast (red); **C** — 3rd contrast (yellow); **D** — 4th contrast (black).

Note — Instructions in square brackets [ ] are worked the number of times stated.

2 sts at start of following 4 rows — 25 sts.

Increase 1 st at each end of next row and following 2 alternate rows, then every following 4th row until there are 37 sts.

Work 9 rows straight.

Decrease 1 st at each end of next row and every following alternate row until 31 sts remain.

Cast off 2 sts at start of next 4 rows, then 3 sts at start of following 2 rows — 17 sts. Cast off.

ARMS (Make 2)

With 3¼ mm needles and M, cast on 26 sts. Work 48 rows in st-st. Break off M, join in C and work 4 rows in st-st.

Shape Hand

Next row — [Skpo, K9, K2 tog] twice.

Next row and every following alternate row — Purl.

Next row — [Skpo, K7, K2 tog] twice.

Continue to decrease in this way until 6 sts remain, ending after a purl row. Cast off.

LEGS (Make 2)

With 3¼ mm needles and A, cast on 56 sts. Work 4 rows in st-st.

Decrease 1 st at each end of next row and following 4th row. Decrease 1 st at each end of every alternate row until 46 sts remain, ending after a purl row.

Cast off 2 sts at start of next 4 rows — 38 sts.

Break off A, join in M. Continue in st-st until work measures 43 cm, *17 ins,* ending after a purl row. Cast off.

Work another leg, but starting with B instead of A.

Sole (Make 2)

With 3¼ mm needles and A, cast on 7 sts. Knit 1 row, purl 1 row.

BODY (Make 2 pieces)

With 3¼ mm needles and M, cast on 47 sts. Work 22 cm, *8¾ ins,* in st-st, ending after a purl row. Cast off.

HEAD (Make 2 pieces)

With 3¼ mm needles and M, cast on 11 sts.

Work 2 rows in st-st. Cast on 3 sts at start of next 2 rows and

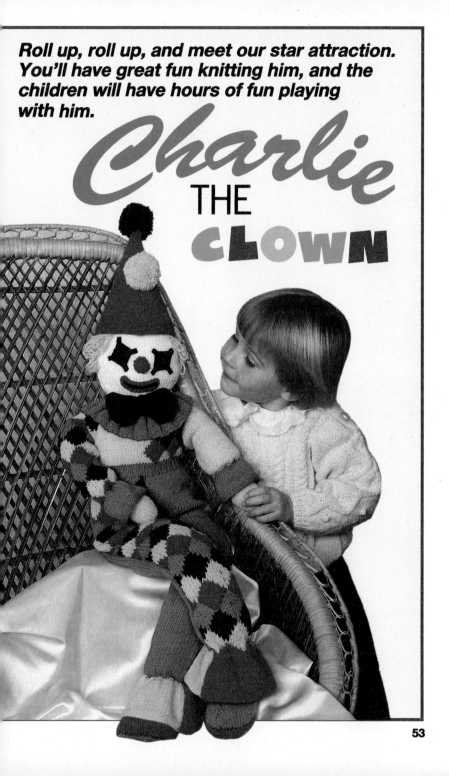

Roll up, roll up, and meet our star attraction. You'll have great fun knitting him, and the children will have hours of fun playing with him.

Charlie THE CLOWN

CHARLIE THE CLOWN

Cast on 2 sts at start of next 2 rows. Increase 1 st at each end of next row and following alternate row, then every following 4th row until there are 19 sts.

Work 9 rows straight.

Decrease 1 st at each end of next row and following 4th row, then every alternate row until 11 sts remain.

Cast off 2 sts at start of next 2 rows.

Work 1 row. Cast off.

Work another sole, but using B instead of A.

TO MAKE UP BODY

Join body seams, leaving openings for arms at sides and legs at bottom. Stuff body firmly. Join head seams and stuff head, then sew to body. Join arm seams, stuff and sew to body, then join leg seams. Sew in the sole, placing A on B and B on A, stuff and sew to body.

HAIR

With 4 mm needles and C, cast on 8 sts. Knit 1 row.

Work in pattern as follows:

1st row — Knit.

2nd row — [K1, loop 1] to end.

Repeat these 2 rows, **at the same time** casting on 2 sts at start of next 2 rows, 4 sts at start of next 2 rows and 6 sts at start of next 2 rows — 32 sts.

Continue in pattern, casting off 6 sts at start of next 2 rows, 4 sts at start of next 2 rows and 2 sts at start of next 2 rows — 8 sts.

Cast off knitwise.

Sew hair to head as shown. Cut out shapes for eyes in black felt and sew to face. Cut out a circle in red felt for nose, stuff and sew to face. Cut out shapes for mouth and sew to face.

SUIT BACK

Left Leg

With 3¼ mm needles and B, cast on 42 sts.

**Work 4 rows in garter-stitch.

CHART 1

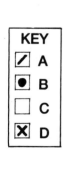

KEY

◰	A
◉	B
☐	C
☒	D

9-STITCH REPEAT (right sleeve)

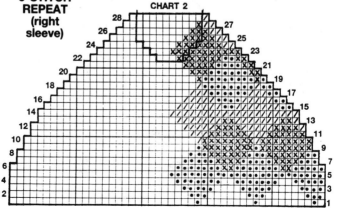

CHART 2

Change to 4 mm needles. Work in st-st for 5 cm, *2 ins*, ending after a knit row.

Decrease row — [P2 tog, P1] 14 times — 28 sts.**

Change to 4½ mm needles and begin pattern from Chart 1, joining in and breaking off colours as required. Strand yarn loosely across back of work to avoid pulling it in.

On Chart, read odd-numbered knit rows from right to left and even-numbered purl rows from left to right.

Repeat the 18 rows of Chart 1 until leg measures 37 cm, *14½ ins*, ending after a purl row.

Leave sts on a holder but do NOT break off yarns.

Right Leg

With 3¼ mm needles and C, cast on 42 sts. Work as for left leg from ** to **.

Change to 4½ mm needles.

Break off C, join in A. Continue in st-st until work measures 37 cm, *14½ ins*, ending after a purl row.

Next row — With 4 mm needles, knit across all sts from both needles — 56 sts. **Note** — When working across sts from left leg, work in pattern.

Continue in pattern as set until work measures 48 cm, *19 ins*, ending after a knit row.

Decrease row — P2, [P2 tog, P1] 18 times — 38 sts.

Change to 3¼ mm needles and A. Work 7 rows in K1, P1 rib, ending after a wrong-side row.

Increase row — Rib 1, *m1, rib 4, repeat from * to last st, m1, rib 1 — 48 sts.

Change to 4 mm needles. Work first 6 rows from Chart 2, ending after a purl row.***

Shape Raglan Armholes

Decrease 1 st at each end of

next row and every following alternate row as shown on Chart until row 14 has been completed — 40 sts.

Divide For Opening

Next row — Work 2 tog, pattern 18, turn and leave remaining 20 sts on a spare needle.

Continue to work from Chart, decreasing at raglan edge on every row until 6 sts remain. Cast off.

Return to sts on spare needle. With right side of work facing, join in C. Knit to last 2 sts, K2 tog.

Complete to match first side, reversing shaping.

SUIT FRONT

Work as given for suit back to ***, reading left for right and right for left throughout.

Shape raglan armholes as shown on Chart 2, but omitting back opening and shaping neck as shown by thick line, casting off centre 4 sts at neck.

Left Sleeve

With 3¼ mm needles and A, cast on 48 sts. Work 4 rows in garter-stitch. Change to 4 mm needles. Continue in st-st for 3 cm, *1¼ ins*, ending after a knit row.

Decrease row — P1, [P2 tog, P2] 11 times, P2 tog, P1 — 36 sts.

Break off A, join in C and work 11 cm, *4¼ ins*, in st-st, ending after a purl row.

Shape Raglan

Decrease 1 st at each end of next row and every following alternate row until 24 sts remain, then every row until 4 sts remain. Cast off.

Right Sleeve

Work as for left sleeve until

CHARLIE THE CLOWN

decrease row is completed — 36 sts.

Change to 4½ mm needles. Repeat the 9 pattern sts indicated on Chart 1 for 11 cm, *4¼ ins,* ending after a purl row.

Shape Raglan

Complete as given for left sleeve, repeating the 18 rows of Chart 1 throughout.

With 4 mm needles and A, cast on 15 sts. Knit 1 row.

1st row — Knit.
2nd row — P12, turn.
3rd row — K12.
4th row — P12, K3.
5th row — K3, P12.
6th row — K12, turn.
7th row — P12.
8th row — Knit.

Repeat these 8 rows until shorter edge of frill fits round neck edge, ending after a 4th row. Cast off.

BOW-TIE

With 4 mm needles and D, cast on 44 sts.

Knit 1 row.

Beginning with a knit row, continue in st-st for 6 cm, *2¼ ins,* ending after a knit row.

Cast off knitwise.

With 4 mm needles and D, cast on 11 sts. Work 4 rows in garter-stitch. Cast off.

Fold shorter ends together and join seam.

Gather centre and sew the small piece round centre, fastening at the back.

HAT

With firm card, cut out a semi-circle with a diameter of 18 cm, *7 ins.* Fold round to make a cone and secure with Sellotape.

With 4 mm needles and B, cast on 8 sts. Knit 1 row, purl 1 row.

Continue in st-st, casting on 3 sts at start of next 16 rows — 56 sts.

Decrease 1 st at each end of next row and every following alternate row until 42 sts remain. Cast off 2 sts at start of every row until 2 sts remain. Work 2 tog and fasten off.

With right side of work facing, 3¼ mm needles and B, pick up and knit 70 sts all round lower edge of hat. Work 4 rows in garter-stitch. Cast off.

Join side seam, then tack to card cone. Make 2 pom-poms with other colours and sew to hat. Sew a piece of elastic to each side of hat to fit head.

TO MAKE UP SUIT

Join raglan seams.

Work one row of double crochet round back opening, making 3 buttonhole loops on right-hand side. Sew buttons to other side to match.

Join side and sleeve seams, then join inside leg seams. Cut elastic to fit arms and legs, and join to form a ring. Work a herringbone casing over elastic at each frill on arms and legs. Sew frill round neck and sew bow-tie on top. ■

Continued from page 51.

"What if something does?"

"It won't. Look, Brian is nearly eighteen. He can look after everything, and Neil and Anna aren't children any more."

"They'll always be children to me," she said dejectedly.

He sighed. "I didn't expect clichés with my bacon and egg."

"You're just irresponsible," she protested. "Some caring parent you are."

"I *do* care," he declared. "I just want to forget for a fortnight. Is it so much to ask?"

"I suppose not," she said reluctantly.

He finished his tea, putting the cup down with a flourish.

"Will you give it a rest? Come out on the sands. Let's go beachcombing. Maybe we'll find something washed up by the tide."

"Like oil?' she asked.

"You know the saying 'I'll enjoy myself if it kills me'?" he asked. She nodded.

"Well, 'it' may not kill you." He smiled sweetly. "But I will."

For the next few days, Valerie made up her mind to do exactly that, enjoy herself despite her worries.

It dawned on her that she must look a bit of an idiot anyway, acting as if she couldn't bear to be away from her domestic problems.

She decided she would show everyone that she was just as capable as Peter of forgetting her children for a fortnight.

They went to places and saw sights they hadn't seen for eighteen years. Some places were a little more built up, others weren't there any more, but the coastline was the same.

The sea still crashed in, scouring the grey, granite cliffs, and the sun shone out of cloudless blue skies for hours on end. For April the weather was exceptional.

Soon a week of the holiday was nearly gone.

Despite herself, Valerie felt the niggle of worry every time they passed a phone-box.

As they went about, she watched Peter. He was as merry as the young man she'd first met twenty years ago, enjoying his freedom and lavishing all his care and attention on her. She couldn't help feeling just a twinge of distaste.

He had so obviously just banished the children from his thoughts.

If he mentioned them in passing, it was only to say how

57

SECOND HONEYMOON

marvellous it was not to have them around.

It was as if they didn't have a family any more, as if all that child-bearing and bringing them up had gone for nothing.

One afternoon, she made up her mind that, the first chance which came along, she would phone home to make sure everything was all right.

She would do it while Peter wasn't about.

ONE evening, about half past six, they had come in from a long walk along the cliffs. Valerie was stretched out on the sofa, flicking through a magazine. Her hair was tied back with a ribbon. She looked younger and fitter, her face glowing from the sun and sea air.

Peter ambled about the room restlessly. He picked up a book that lay on the table and took it across to the window. He read a few pages, standing there, then closed the book.

"That was a waste of money."

"Not very good?" she enquired, looking up.

"Terrible. Should have known by the cover."

"Never mind. There are some more by the bed."

He leaned against the window frame, looking out at the calm sea.

"Think I'll stroll down for a paper before we eat," he said. "Do you want to come?"

"What? Oh, no thanks. I'm sleepy after all that walking. I'll stay here."

"OK." He put on a light jacket, gathered up his cigarettes, lighter, money and other bits and pieces. He paused for a moment in the doorway.

"Sure?"

"Sure," she said.

"Right. I'll be back in about twenty minutes."

" 'Bye." She gave him a little wave.

He seemed to take an age to leave the hotel. She peered out of the window for five minutes or more until, finally, he appeared below, going down the steps to the road. She watched until he was out of sight round a corner, heading for the harbour.

Then it took her a few more minutes to decide that, yes, she would phone while he was out. She sat on the edge of her chair, looking at the telephone, stark and lonely on its own little table.

She thought, you haven't even got the guts to just come out and say, "I want to phone home. It'll make me feel better."

Why? Because you don't want him to call you a soft old fool, that's why . . . Him and his independence.

She picked up the receiver, holding it as if it might explode at any second, and keeping her eyes on the door. The switchboard operator came on the line.

"Good evening," she said. "This is Mrs Morley, room fifteen."

"Oh, hello, Mrs Morley." It was the manager's wife who handled the switchboard as well as reception. Valerie had spoken to her several times in passing. "What can I do for you?"

"I'd like to make an outside call, please."

"Certainly. What's the number?"

She reeled off the six figures of the number, tapping the table nervously with the fingers of one hand.

"Now isn't that funny."

"Isn't what funny?" Valerie asked anxiously.

"That is your home number, isn't it?"

"Yes, yes it is. How did you know that?"

"Well, Mr Morley was just down here in the foyer calling the same number himself."

"He what?"

"Yes, he was making his usual call . . . to settle his nerves, as he says."

"What . . . he's called home before, then?" Valerie was trying very hard to keep her voice at a normal level.

"Oh, once a day, without fail, since the first day you arrived. He told me the other day he wouldn't be able to sleep if he didn't know the family were all safe and sound."

"Of all the . . . " Valerie began.

"He must be a very caring father," the other woman said.

"You could say that." The moment of righteous indignation was fading now. With it went the fear of being caught. A calm little smile replaced the tense expression of a moment before.

"Right then. I'll just put the call through for you."

"Never mind, there's no need now," Valerie said, leaning back easily in her chair. "Not if my husband's already seen to it. Thank you anyway."

"Fine. Anything else I can do for you?"

"No, thank you. Not a thing."

She replaced the receiver slowly, still smiling.

The only good thing about his underhand behaviour was that it showed he actually did care. But really, that pride of his. Was he going to show that he was worried about the children? No way!

Men are so silly sometimes, she thought, laughing, loving Peter for being one of the silliest.

She went and lay down on the bed. Suddenly, she was perfectly calm and happy within. She could go on and enjoy the rest of the holiday, secure in the knowledge that her poor, dear husband was doing all her fretting for her.

Of course, she would never tell Peter that she knew. If he discovered that he had been found out it would spoil the holiday. It was better to keep it to herself.

Besides, she thought, with a satisfied little grin, it was nice to have some secrets in a marriage. □

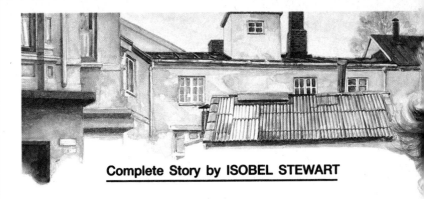

Complete Story by ISOBEL STEWART

HE liked to watch Emily when she was practising. Her small, absorbed face, her grey eyes dreamy behind the glasses she needed to read the music, her small hands, confident and assured on the bow. As he listened to the clear, pure notes, Mark thought of how it would be in a few years, when Emily would be giving violin recitals.

She always went on playing long after her set practising time, and this extra time pleased him even more. It proved — if any proof was needed — that he was right, that her music was the one thing that mattered most in the world to her.

She didn't talk about her mother much now. Even after Diana's brief visits, Emily didn't seem to find it strange or upsetting that her mother should visit them, then leave, as if she was a stranger.

He had, of course, explained to Emily when Diana left, and Emily was a reasonable child. She had listened while Mark told her that her mother had been promoted at work, and that as it was too far to travel every day she had decided to have a small flat in London.

Emily had asked only one question.

"Will I see Mummy again?"

"Of course you will," Mark had said, his heart aching for her. "She'll come to see us when she has time."

Sometimes Mark wondered what he would say if Emily asked him if they were getting divorced. He had decided to be honest, and say that at the moment there was no question of divorce — it was just that it seemed better for all of them to have some time apart.

But Emily never mentioned the word divorce. He wondered, sometimes, if any of her friends at school asked her, but it seemed better, since she said nothing herself, just to leave the whole question.

She was a strange mixture, this daughter of his, he sometimes thought. Where her music was concerned, she was practical and business-like. In most other things she seemed younger than her

What's best for EMILY

As her father, he was sure he knew best. He never stopped to wonder if perhaps he could be wrong.

twelve years, vague and dreamy. Quiet and reserved, seldom showing her feelings.

That was why he was so surprised when she came hurrying in from school one day, her face aglow. Mark looked at her, taken aback by a fleeting resemblance to Diana in the early years of their marriage, bright, eager, excited. Not as she had become later, cool and remote.

"Daddy," Emily said excitedly, "there's a nature ramble on Saturday. Miss Martin is taking the whole class."

"Who's Miss Martin?" Mark asked, playing for time.

"My new teacher. I told you about her," Emily reminded him. "Daddy, it's going to be such fun — we have to leave early, right after breakfast."

Mark took a deep breath. "Emily," he said carefully, "you know we can't let you go on a — a nature ramble. Remember the time you went to the zoo, and you fell and hurt your hands? You had to miss an exam that time. We can't risk it with your next exam only four weeks away."

Emily looked at him, the light slowly fading from her eyes.

"I wouldn't hurt my hands," she said, not quite steadily. "I — I would be careful, Daddy. And Miss Martin would look after me."

Mark shook his head. "It's out of the question, Emily. I've got to think of your future. You do understand that, don't you? You have a gift and it's worth giving up some of the little things to make the most of it."

She didn't argue, and he was glad of that. Instead, she lifted up her school satchel and carried it through to her room.

BY the time she had finished her homework, Mark had tea ready. After that Emily, as always, did her practising, then got ready for bed. She didn't watch television during the week, for she rose early to practise for half an hour before school.

Mark looked out the papers he had brought home from the office, and went to say goodnight. At Emily's door, he stopped, appalled. She was crying, not noisily, but so quietly and hopelessly that it tore at his heart.

For the first time since Diana had left, he wished that she was there. She would have known what to do.

He sat down on the bed and put his hands on his daughter's shoulders.

"Emily," he said gently, "don't be so upset, love. You know there are things you have to give up because of your music. This is just one of them."

"But everyone's going," Emily replied, her voice muffled and tearful. "And — and what will Miss Martin think of me if I'm the only one who doesn't go?"

Mark felt a wave of relief. If that was the only problem . . . He could deal with that.

"I'll go and talk to Miss Martin myself," he said. "I'll explain."

Emily had stopped crying. She sat up and looked at him.

"If you're explaining to her about Saturday, will you tell her it was because of my practising that I couldn't watch the TV programme about the Crusaders that she wanted us to see last week? Remember, Daddy?"

Mark did remember.

"I'll tell her." He hugged her warm little body to him for a moment, then kissed her forehead. "Now go to sleep, Emily, and don't worry about it. I'll go and see her tomorrow afternoon."

OLD dragon, he thought, as he crossed the rapidly-emptying playground next day. She'll have to realise that Emily is different.

He knocked on the classroom door, and a voice told him to come in.

The girl at the desk was small, slim and auburn-haired. She looked up at Mark, her blue eyes warm and friendly.

"Yes?"

"Miss Martin?" When the girl nodded, Mark pulled himself together. "Miss Martin, I'm Emily's father — Mark Bennett."

"Yes, Mr Bennett?" Her eyes were less friendly now. "I'll be interested to hear why Emily is the only child in my class who isn't coming on our nature ramble on Saturday."

Mark hadn't expected a direct confrontation. But he recovered quickly, and began to explain to Miss Martin.

He told her what Professor Fellini thought of Emily's playing, and he told her how she had astonished the examiners each time. He also explained that Emily had another exam very soon, which was why she was practising so intensively, and why she had had to miss the Crusader programme.

"She could have practised at a different time, Mr Bennett," Miss Martin said crisply. "And I fail to see why any of this should stop Emily coming on my nature ramble on Saturday."

"Emily is a gifted child," Mark pointed out.

Miss Martin's blue eyes looked back at him, unwavering. "Emily is first and foremost a child."

"She might hurt her hands," Mark explained. "She might sprain her wrist, she might get a cut that becomes infected. I can't risk anything that might spoil her future."

"No, I don't suppose you can," she replied unexpectedly. "Why don't you come along with us, Mr Bennett, then you can keep an eye on Emily for yourself?"

Ten minutes later, Mark walked back to his car, not quite sure why he had agreed to Miss Martin's suggestion.

Emily was delighted when he told her, but Mark was already wishing he had said no.

WHAT'S BEST FOR EMILY

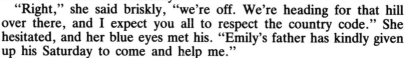

ON the Saturday morning, there he was, Mark Bennett, respected lawyer in the small market town, setting off on a nature ramble with a school-teacher and thirty twelve-year-olds.

Miss Martin was wearing jeans and a checked shirt, and her hair was tied back casually.

"Right," she said briskly, "we're off. We're heading for that hill over there, and I expect you all to respect the country code." She hesitated, and her blue eyes met his. "Emily's father has kindly given up his Saturday to come and help me."

They walked over the fields towards the hill, the children straggling in small groups, talking and laughing.

Emily stayed beside her father until Miss Martin took her to the group nearest, walked with them for a little while, then dropped back. Emily remained with the other children.

Mark looked at Miss Martin with respect. "You did that well." He hesitated. "Emily does seem to have problems mixing with other children."

"She does." Miss Martin looked at him. "I'm concerned about Emily. This isn't the time for it, but — could we have a talk?"

"I don't think it's necessary," Mark said.

Unexpectedly, Miss Martin put her hand on his arm.

"Mr Bennett, I'm fond of Emily. I'm fond of all my children, but — I really am concerned about her."

Mark saw that she meant it.

"Monday after school?" he suggested. "Emily has her music lesson then, so if you'd like to come round to the house . . ."

"Thank you, Mr Bennett." She smiled.

At first, he watched Emily anxiously, particularly when the children climbed a fence or ran down a hillside. But he saw that Emily was, as she had promised, being careful. He relaxed then, and to his surprise began to join in some of the games.

When it was over, and they separated at school in the late afternoon, he looked at his daughter. Her hair was a mess and her face was dirty, but she was smiling.

"Thank you, Miss Martin, it was a lovely day."

"I enjoyed it, too, Emily. I'm so glad you could come," Miss Martin said.

Mark hesitated, but only for a moment. "I enjoyed it as well, Miss Martin. Thank you."

Monday came, and Emily had gone for her music lesson. Mark boiled the kettle, ready to make tea, and set out a tray. Thanks to Mrs Wilkes, who came on Monday, Wednesday and Friday, the place always looked clean, and Emily was a tidy child. It was Diana who had been untidy, living each moment as it came.

He sighed. Funny that he should almost miss that kind of thing.

"Did you come home from your office specially early, Mr Bennett?" Miss Martin asked, when he opened the door. "Where should I put my bike?"

"Just leave it there," Mark said. "No, I always come home for Emily coming out of school. I bring work home with me."

He closed the door and led the way to the lounge.

"It must be nice living here," she said, looking around. "I tried for a flat here, too, but I believe there are only five, and they're all bigger than I want."

When she was seated, he poured tea for them, and offered her a scone.

"Lovely." She smiled. "Did Emily make them?"

He looked at her, surprised.

"I don't let Emily do anything like that. She might —"

"Hurt her hands," Miss Martin finished for him. She put down her half-eaten scone, and Mark could see the determination in her face. "Mr Bennett, you're not being fair to Emily."

"It may look that way to you," Mark said, but the girl's eyes were warm and blue, and his resentment began to fade as he told her about Emily and his hopes for her future.

AT some point he and Miss Martin became Mark and Julie. The warmth in Julie's blue eyes made it easy to go on from there, to tell her about the growing trouble between Diana and him over Emily's music.

"It wasn't that she was against Emily concentrating on her music," he said. "She just kept saying that Emily must have the chance to do other things, too. She wouldn't see that unless Emily puts everything into her music she won't make it."

"I haven't heard Emily play," Julie said, "but so many people have told me she has a gift.

"But, Mark, have you thought — if this gift of Emily's doesn't take her to the top, then — because you've shut everything else out of Emily's life — she'll be left with nothing."

"Diana says that, too," he admitted reluctantly. "It's a valid point. That's why it's so important to me to help her make it — and she will."

Julie's rounded chin was determined. "And if she doesn't? What is she going to make of her life? Look, Mark, I've been concerned about Emily from the moment I walked into that class. She's withdrawn from the other children, she has no friends, she just isn't part of the class. She's lonely, Mark."

"Emily doesn't need other children." He spoke with a conviction he wasn't feeling. "What would she have in common with them?"

"I don't know," Julie admitted, "but maybe she'd like the chance to find out!"

He saw her take a deep breath.

"And another thing," she went on, "Emily misses her mother."

He stared at her in surprise. "Emily never even mentions her mother. Even when Diana comes to visit her, Emily doesn't talk about her at all. I ask if she's had a nice time with her mother, and she says yes, and — that's it."

"That's because she misses her. She's afraid to talk about her, afraid to think about her. It's all going on inside, Mark, and — that isn't good. Emily shouldn't be as — as self-contained as she is, at twelve years old. Look, she isn't the only child from a broken home in my class, but she's the only one who reacts this way."

"Emily is different," he said stubbornly.

"That she is." Julie sighed. "Won't you let me try to do what I can, to make her more — more like a normal child? Would you ease the pressure a little, and let her take part in some of the things the other children do?"

The clock chimed. Soon Emily would be home from her music lesson.

"She has an exam soon," Mark pointed out.

"And if she gets ninety per cent. instead of ninety-five per cent.?" Gently, she put her hand on his. "Please — let me try. For Emily's sake."

He hesitated, weakening now. "What were you thinking of doing?"

"I don't really know. There is the class play — Emily said she wouldn't have time to take part, because rehearsals are after school. Now Susan has dropped out — she has measles — I could put Emily in her part. It isn't a big part, she wouldn't have too much learning to do, but — I think she'd enjoy it.

"I'd also like to get her on my roster for visiting Margaret, who's in hospital. I get the children to visit her two at a time, because she's going to be there for a long spell."

She smiled, and he realised that her hand was still on his.

"That's just for starters. Please, Mark."

It didn't seem much to ask. Suddenly he realised it was exactly the sort of thing Diana had wanted for Emily.

"All right," he said, smiling back at her. "But if her music starts to suffer, then — the deal's off."

"I'm sure it won't," Julie assured him, her face alight.

Over the next few weeks, he had to admit that Julie was as good as her word. He had to adjust Emily's practising time, and occasionally it had to be cut short, but there was no doubt that she was playing every bit as well as she always had. And when the exam was over, she was quietly confident that she had done well.

Mark found himself getting into the habit of dropping in at the play rehearsals, so that he could take Emily home afterwards. He had to admit that Julie had been right. Emily was loving this. In spite of her solemn manner, she had an undoubted gift for comedy.

"She's good." There was mischief in Julie's blue eyes. "Have you unsuspected acting talents, Mark?"

"None at all." He smiled. He looked at his daughter on the stage. "Diana used to enjoy amateur dramatics," he said thoughtfully. "I suppose Emily has inherited her talent for it."

Diana. He'd almost forgotten how droll she'd sometimes been in the early years of their marriage.

MARK began to offer Julie a lift home after rehearsals. He wasn't sure if it was himself or Emily who first invited her to come and have tea with them. It soon became a regular event, and one that Mark found himself looking forward to.

When they had finished, Emily would start practising, and Julie and Mark would go through to the kitchen to wash the dishes.

Mark found it was surprisingly easy to talk to Julie about Diana. Sometimes he was surprised at the way Julie's different outlook made him admit that he had often been the one at fault, and not his wife.

Diana's career, for one thing. Mark had blamed her career in advertising as one of the things that had led to the breakdown of their marriage.

Diana had loved her job but, as Julie pointed out, she had given it up willingly for him and Emily.

Once, he asked Julie about boyfriends, unable to believe that there was no-one special.

"Oh yes," she told him readily. "There's Tony — he's the P.E. teacher — I go out with him quite often. And there's David, he's a doctor."

"David Wilson?" Mark asked, surprised.

"Yes. Then there's Steve, he's a farmer."

"Safety in numbers, eh?" Mark laughed.

Yet it was a surprisingly disturbing thought, Julie with any of these three men, and Mark was glad when a wrong note from Emily made him break off the conversation.

A WEEK before the play, Emily had flu. She was flushed and tearful in the morning, and Mark made her stay in bed. He phoned the school, and he phoned his office.

Emily slept a lot, but each time she woke he made her a hot lemon and honey drink, the kind Diana always made for colds.

Soon after four, Julie came, and Mark took her through. Emily was asleep but restless. Julie sat down beside her, and put her hand on Emily's flushed forehead. The child stirred.

"Mummy?" she said drowsily. "I'm so glad you came."

Across the room Julie's eyes met Mark's.

"It's not your mummy," he said. "It's Miss Martin."

Emily opened her eyes. "Oh." There was no mistaking the disappointment in her voice, before she woke properly, and remembered to be polite. "Thank you for coming, Miss Martin. I'll be better for the play, really I will."

"Of course you will, Emily. You sleep as much as you can. That's the best thing, my mother always says that."

Emily smiled. "So does mine." She closed her eyes.

A few minutes later, Julie came through to where Mark was sitting at the fire, studying papers without seeing them, trying to forget the look on his daughter's face, the longing in her voice when she'd said, "Mummy."

"She's asleep." Julie smiled. "But she finished her hot drink."

Mark stood up and took the glass from her. In the kitchen, he washed it and rinsed it carefully, and set it on the draining-board.

When he turned round, Julie was watching him. There was something in her blue eyes — something unguarded, defenceless, that told him how she would feel in his arms. Soft and small and warm. He stepped forward.

"Julie?"

Colour rose in her cheeks. "I think I should go."

For an endless moment, Mark fought the instinct that told him to

68

take her in his arms. But her blue eyes held his steadily, and after a moment she turned and went out.

Yes, Julie, you were right to go, he thought with sadness.

IT was two days before Emily could go back to school. Julie had rehearsals for the play after school both days. She telephoned, though, and spoke to Emily, reassuring her that the part was still there for her. But she didn't come to the house and Mark didn't know whether to be relieved or sorry.

The day before the play he was held up by a client, and reached school just as the rehearsal finished. The children came out together, talking eagerly, and Mark saw that Emily was part of the group, no longer on the outside looking in.

Across the room, he saw Julie watching, too. She smiled at him.

"Can I give you a lift?" he asked, as casually as he could.

She shook her head. "I brought my bike to school today.

"Mark, I'm glad you came. I wanted to see you. I — I wanted to ask if you couldn't bring Emily's mother to the play tomorrow night."

"Are you trying to patch things up between Diana and me?" Mark asked, uncertain whether to laugh or be angry.

Julie's chin tilted. "Maybe I am. Maybe you need some pushing towards that. You know what I think, Mark? I think neither you nor Diana tried hard enough. I think you could really make a go of your marriage if you tried again."

"For Emily's sake?" he asked, and knew that she, too, was remembering that moment when he had so nearly kissed her.

"Yes, for Emily's sake." She flushed. "But — but for your own sakes, too, Mark. You once loved Diana, she once loved you. Look, Mark, just ask her to come and see Emily in the play. That's all. Just for —"

"For starters?" He smiled. "You're a real teacher, Julie, a bossy little thing! Maybe I wasn't so far wrong when I thought of you as a dragon before I met you."

"I can be when it's necessary." She locked the classroom door, and he walked with her to her bike. "Just try, Mark."

"What if Diana doesn't want to come?"

"I think she will," Julie said, and he had a sudden conviction that she was right.

He looked down at her, her auburn hair blowing in the wind as she stood beside him. "What about you, Julie?"

She hesitated. "I'm not sure. But — David wants me to visit his folk with him in the holidays. They live in Devon, and his father wants to retire, but only if David — David thinks there might be a job for me at the local school, if I was interested."

"And — are you interested?"

"I think I could be — once we were away from here," she said, her voice low. "I — I think it would be better for David and I to get to know each other properly, somewhere different. I'm going, anyway, and — we'll see."

She looked up at him again. "Mark — phone Diana, ask her to come to the play."

"All right," he agreed. Standing there beside her, the aching uncertainty of what might have been was suddenly too much for him. Abruptly, he turned away, so that he didn't have to watch her cycle away from him.

AT home, he let Emily help him to get tea ready, as she had been doing more and more often now. When they were sitting at the table, he made up his mind.

"Emily, would you like me to phone Mummy and ask her if she can come to the play tomorrow?"

The blazing joy in Emily's face told him that Julie had been right. Then almost visibly, Emily drew back, and became once again composed, careful.

"That would be nice," she replied sedately. Then, the composure cracking just a little, "Do you — do you think she'll come, Daddy?"

He smiled at her. "I think so. Let's phone right now and ask her."

He dialled the number of Diana's flat, then stood waiting, with one arm around Emily.

The ringing stopped.

"Hello?" Diana said.

His arm tightened around his daughter. "Diana, it's Mark. Emily is in a school play tomorrow, and we wondered — at least — we thought — we'd like you to come and see it."

He hadn't intended to sound so unsure of himself, but it had been more difficult than he had thought. It wasn't just the play, it was Emily, it was himself, it was any chance they might have of finding happiness together again.

"Mark?" Diana said, and his heart turned over at the uncertainty in her voice. "Do you — want me to come?"

There was no hesitation now. "Yes, I want you to come."

"Then I will," Diana said quietly. "I'll clear things up here, and I'll be with you tomorrow about lunchtime. Is that all right?"

"Yes. That's fine. Do you want to speak to Emily?"

"Please," Diana said.

He handed the receiver to Emily.

"Hello, Mummy," Emily said, and happiness soared in her voice. "I'm so glad you're coming tomorrow."

So am I, Mark thought, with growing certainty. So am I. And as he waited for Emily to finish telling her mother about the play, he thought, with deep gratitude — thank you, Julie.

Some day, maybe, I'll be able to say it properly. But tomorrow, all I'll be able to do is look at you across the room and say it silently — thank you, Julie. □

Complete Story

by ALISON REDFORD

For him there had never been anyone quite like Laura, until the day her daughter walked into his life.

IT was so long since he had thought of Laura. Years, probably, Adam realised with surprise. It must be more than 20 years since he had seen her, and he certainly hadn't spent those years thinking about her.

Oh, there had been moments of regret — but regret was pointless, and gradually, over the years, he had thought less and less often of Laura.

So why, he wondered, half amused, half exasperated, was he thinking of her now?

Megan, he thought. That's it. There was something about Megan, the new typist, that reminded him of Laura. Brown hair, grey eyes, same colouring. Not that that was very unusual.

"Thanks, Megan," he said, as she handed him his coffee.

I Remember Laura

I REMEMBER LAURA

She smiled, and he thought in surprise — but her smile is exactly like Laura's.

"Is there something wrong, Mr Ward?" she asked uncertainly.

Adam shook his head. "No, Megan, it's just — for a moment you reminded me of someone."

She coloured. "I wonder — I didn't like to say, Mr Ward, but I think you once knew my mother. She used to work here. She said to me, 'Ask Mr Ward if he remembers Laura'."

Adam looked at her. Her eyes — her smile — the dimple on her chin. He shouldn't have needed to be told that this was Laura's daughter.

"Oh, yes, Megan," he said softly. "Tell her that I remember her very clearly."

He wanted to ask Megan about her mother, but before he could say anything, the senior typist, Jean, knocked on his door.

"Oh, there you are, Megan. Mr Carson is in a hurry for his coffee."

Megan went out, her cheeks flushed, but Adam caught Jean before she followed.

"Jean — wait," he said quickly. "Did you know that Megan is Laura's daughter? You remember Laura Taylor?"

Jean nodded. "Apart from yourself," she reminded him, "I'm about the only one who would. Yes, Megan told me yesterday, but she was too shy to ask you if you remembered her mother."

She smiled. "I know you don't mean to, Adam, but you do make these girls nervous."

"Do I?" Adam asked, surprised. "I don't make you nervous, Jean."

"No, you don't," she agreed. "But I've known you for a long time. More than twenty years."

Adam looked at her. An efficient worker and a likeable person, Jean had been part of his office life for so long that he couldn't remember a time at work without her.

"Twenty years is a long time," he said slowly.

Twenty years ago, he thought, you and I and Laura were all young people here together. Laura and Jean, the two most junior typists, and himself a struggling clerk.

Now he was managing director, Jean was head typist, and Laura — Laura was the mother of this girl, Megan. Megan Jones, wasn't it? Of course, he remembered now, David Jones was the name of the man Laura had married.

Jean would be — what? — 38 or 39, he realised with surprise. He hadn't noticed any real change in her. Her dark hair was still short and curly, her hazel eyes friendly, she was as slim as she had always been.

It was a wonder that she hadn't married, he thought, not for the first time — but, as always, with relief, for she was an excellent and efficient head typist. There had been men in her life, he knew, through the years. The young fellow from the bank, always waiting for Jean. Then Ted Peters who had been transferred to Manchester.

"Hey, come back, Adam," Jean said, smiling. "You're miles away."

"Not miles, years," he admitted. "It just shook me, finding that Megan is Laura's daughter."

If I had married Laura, she could have been my daughter, he thought. It was a strange thought, strange and disturbing.

"You don't look twenty years older to me," he said. "Do I look twenty years older to you?"

Jean flushed. "We're so used to each other, it's difficult to say. I certainly don't feel that I'm almost forty — at least I didn't until Megan told me she was Laura's daughter."

She took his cup. "If you want that report before five, I'll have to get it done," she told him.

WHEN she had gone, Adam went back to the sales analysis he had been working on, finding it unusually difficult to keep his mind on his work. It was a relief when Jean brought him the report at five, and he could sign it, and let her post it as she went home.

Usually he worked on for another hour or so when the office was quiet, but tonight he didn't feel like doing that. Instead, he walked across the park to collect his car, although it took five minutes longer that way.

He knew, of course, why he was going this way. Because more than 20 years ago two young people had walked this way every evening, hand in hand, not even noticing whether it was warm and sunny or windy and wet.

It was strange, all these years with hardly a thought of Laura, and now he could almost feel her hand in his, almost see her brown hair bouncing on her shoulders.

Adam Ward, he told himself, you're becoming sentimental in your old age. Twenty years is certainly a long time, just as you said to Jean. You've been perfectly happy with your career and your bachelor life all these years — so what's the point in getting all nostalgic now?

But that didn't do anything to get rid of the way he was feeling. By the time he had made himself a snack, eaten, and efficiently stacked the dishes in the small dishwasher, he had surrendered completely to his mood of nostalgia.

Oh yes, he thought once again. I remember Laura . . .

The first time I saw her she came to the Shipping Department, where I worked. She'd typed a letter for my boss, Mr Newton, and had forgotten to take a copy of it for filing.

I REMEMBER LAURA

W HEN she came out of his office, I couldn't help seeing how distressed she was, and I asked her what was wrong.

"That's not so bad," I told her. "You can do it again right now."

"I know," she agreed sadly. "But this is the second time, and I've been here a month now. He — he shouted at me."

"He does, but he forgets it. I bet when you bring along the retyped letter with the copy, he won't even remember."

She went off then, looking doubtful, but she was smiling when she came out of my boss's office half an hour later. She was a pretty little thing, I thought. Maybe I'd see what she was doing on Friday night.

"No, thank you, Adam," she said, politely but very firmly, when I asked her.

I looked at her, surprised, because I wasn't accustomed to girls turning me down.

"Have you got another date?" I asked abruptly.

"No, I haven't, but . . ."

"But what?" I asked, more determined than ever.

"But I don't think I should go out with you." She hesitated, then, her cheeks flushed, she told me that she had been warned about me by the others.

"Warned about me?" I asked, more amused than annoyed. "Tell me more."

She did. She told me that Margaret, the head typist, and Rina in Despatch, and Moyra in Accounts, had all told her that I was the office Romeo, that I always took out new girls, dated them a few times, then dropped them.

They had also said she should remember she was only 18, and I was 24.

I laughed, of course. Well, what else could I do, with this small, brown-haired girl telling me so earnestly just what a dangerous fellow I was?

"I only want to take you dancing," I told her. "I'm not planning to carry you off to Gretna Green or anything."

"I didn't think you were," Laura said stiffly.

Well, she came out with me, and we went dancing. I liked dancing, I was a good dancer, and to be truthful, Laura hadn't had much experience of dancing.

"Relax," I told her softly. "Just let me lead, and you follow. Don't get nervous. I'm not going to eat you."

I still get a kick when I think of some of the songs we danced to, that time, and all the times that followed. They are the songs that still bring a light to the eyes of people who were dancing in those days.

Give Me A Kiss To Build A Dream On was one. *Don't Let The Stars Get In Your Eyes. All The Way. Walking My Baby Back Home.*

And *Unforgettable.*

That was our tune.

I'm not too sure now why that particular one became our tune, but it did. We danced to it, we hummed to it while we danced, and when the lights were low we kissed to it.

Now, looking back, I wonder why this one girl, of all the girls I'd known, became so special to me. We walked through the park, hand in hand. It was spring, and the first blossom was on the trees, and the birds were building nests.

WE spent our lunch-hour together, always. We'd have a sandwich and a cup of coffee, then we'd walk. In the sunshine or in the rain, it didn't matter.

Sometimes we talked, sometimes we didn't. Sometimes we kissed, and sometimes we didn't. Just being together was all that mattered to us.

It was a good time, that spring and summer with Laura. I remember the sunshine, and those exhilarating days by the river.

I don't remember — or perhaps I don't want to remember — when things began to change.

All I do know is that although the wonder and the magic of being in love with Laura were still there, there was something more.

There was a feeling of pressure, a growing realisation that Laura expected something of me, something more than I was prepared to give.

She didn't say anything. But she was waiting for me to say something.

When we had kissed goodnight, I would find her grey eyes on my face, a little anxious, a little bewildered. And always waiting.

I could have said it. I even thought of saying it.

One night, when I had just left her, I thought that if I sold my golf clubs I could buy Laura an engagement ring. A year, say, would give us long enough to save up, then we could be married.

Married.

The word, even in my thoughts, brought me up too short. Did I really want to commit myself? Did I really want to sell my golf clubs and start saving? Even for Laura?

Look, I pointed out to myself reasonably, we've only known each other for six months, let's give it time. All right, I'm 24, but she's only 18. She needs time to be certain. I won't rush her.

And so I said nothing. And gradually, Laura became a little cool, a little distant, and sometimes she would draw her hand away from mine as we walked together. It was autumn then, and soon it would be winter.

By winter, it was over. Laura went her way and I went mine. There was no quarrel, there was no definite break, we just gradually stopped seeing each other.

There was a new girl in the typists room, a tall blonde, and I began taking her out. I used to see Laura sometimes with a brown-haired fellow with glasses — a lawyer, someone told me.

Then she left the office to work in a travel agency, and I lost touch with her. I did see her around a few times, and we always greeted each other, but only briefly.

I can't remember now who told me, about a year later, that Laura was married. By then, I'd stifled the occasional feeling of regret that I had let Laura go.

I was beginning to get on in the firm, and I was discovering that the challenge of my job was something that could well occupy most of my time and my thoughts.

And so time passed.

There were other girls, of course, through the years. But I never again came as near to giving up my freedom as I had done with Laura. There was, quite simply, no-one else quite like Laura . . .

YES, Adam thought again, I remember Laura. I'd like to know how she is, after all these years. Tomorrow, I'll ask Megan.

"I suppose you know," he said casually to Laura's daughter the next day, "that I was once in love with your mother?"

"Yes, I do." She smiled shyly. "Dad used to say that it took him quite a while to persuade Mum to forget you and marry him."

Adam cleared his throat. "They're happy, your mother and father?" he asked, because he had to know.

"Oh, yes," Megan said with certainty. "I suppose it's something you take for granted, when you're a child, but now, when — when I'm old enough to know what being in love means, I can see that they're happy.

"Mum always hurries to meet Dad when he comes in, and sometimes I see them look at each other across the room. They don't say anything — I don't think they need to — but it's enough."

Yes. I could believe it is, Adam thought, and felt a wave of sadness and envy that shook him.

"I'm glad she's happy," he said softly, almost to himself. He looked up to find his young typist's eyes on him. "Tell your mother that, will you, Megan? I think she'll understand."

It was a strange day. The memory of Laura, the memory of the way they had felt about each other, was still unsettling him. Once again, he decided to leave earlier than usual.

The typists' room was empty except for Jean, putting the cover on her typewriter.

"You're leaving early," she said, surprised.

"It's too nice a night to work," he told her. "There's a feeling of spring in the air."

Her hazel eyes were kind, and he realised, surprised, that she understood at least a little of what he was feeling.

"Are you having regrets, Adam? Sorry you didn't marry Laura?"

"Perhaps," he admitted.

"Do you want to see her again?"

He shook his head. "No. The Laura of today is a happily-married wife and mother. She's a different person from the Laura I remember.

"No, Jean, I don't think I'm feeling nostalgic about Laura herself, it's more about the way I felt, then. You know — young and in love and the world a wonderful place. It was a good way to feel."

"I know that, too," Jean said, her voice steady.

He remembered how he had wondered why she had never married. Some day, he thought, I'll ask her.

The thought surprised him.

Now, standing beside her, he realised, with growing understanding, that she was no longer the young typist he had known all those years ago, and she was no longer only his efficient right hand.

She was a woman only a few years younger than he was, a woman who had known love, and who had either turned away from it or lost out on it.

A woman who must sometimes be lonely, as he was sometimes lonely.

"Are you in a hurry, Jean?" he asked tentatively.

"I'm afraid I am," she said, and he was surprised at his disappointment.

She smiled, a little uncertainly. "I've got a dog who's a clock-watcher," she told him. "He's a big dog, and my mother can't take him out, so he waits for me. I take him for a walk the moment I get home."

Adam hesitated, but only for a moment.

"Can I walk with you?" he asked.

"If you want to," Jean replied.

He put one hand under her arm. "Yes, I want to," he said, meaning it.

And as they went out of the office together, he thought, with gratitude — thank you, Laura.

For he knew that if it hadn't been for the memory of Laura, the memory of their love, he wouldn't be doing this now.

And he had a strange and satisfying feeling that for Jean, and for himself, this was the first step towards something that could become very important. □

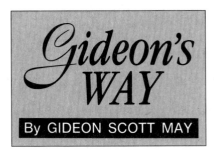

Gideon's WAY

By GIDEON SCOTT MAY

WHEN I fed the poultry flock, the youngest pullet was missing. I knew immediately she wasn't there because there was something special about this bird.

She not only had the scintillating shades of silver in a pedigree plumage but, unlike the others, her legs were attractively feathered right down to the flight feathers that fanned out between her toes.

So I called her "Fairy Feet."

The other birds bullied her quite a bit, not only because she was small and dainty but also, I think, they were jealous of her good looks, trim figure and feathered feet.

Just to make sure that Fairy Feet would thrive and get her fair share at meal times, I put her food in a little coop, so I could close the door when she went in to have her meal in peace.

Chickens, in the main, are classed as brainless birds, but not this one. She was different and quickly learned to pop into the coop for breakfast, without being bothered and bullied by the other birds.

Fairy Feet seemed to recognise me as her protector and, whenever I approached the flock, she came racing towards me like a plane about to take off.

She would daintily pick a piece of toast from my fingers, a treat from our breakfast table, and she knew the moment to take it, when the others weren't looking!

But this morning, Fairy Feet's breakfast of warm meal mash and maize is still lying untouched in the little coop, and has long since grown cold. What, I wonder, could have happened to her?

I had my suspicions. There was a scattering of snow on the hill at the back of the house and I saw, on its glistening surface, the pad marks of a big wild cat.

But they normally distrust and fear the musky smell of man and go out of their way to avoid any contact with humans.

We always make it a rule to have breakfast after everything is fed; the bacon is sizzling in the pan with that tantalising smell that you can only really appreciate after breathing the early-morning air; the eggs, with their rich, red yolks, are being gently basted. I'm sure our birds would all go on strike and stop laying if I turned one of their masterpieces over.

GLANCING out of the kitchen window, I choke over my first mouthful of this delicious fare as I see, almost in slow motion, the lithe big body of a wild cat effortlessly leaping the heathery roadside bank with a bird clasped firmly in its jaws.

One of the young her
at Croft Dougla
simply isn't like any oth
and she holds a ve
special place
Gideon's affections .

I was completely fascinated by the sight of this Highland tiger with its broad, light brown head, striped boldly with black, and crowned with a pair of tufted ears laid flat back as if they had gone to an early bed.

There was a golden glow in the cat's eyes as it turned to take an almost insolent look at me, before disappearing under a blanket of bronze bracken with its burden.

But what about the bird in its mouth?

I thought, at first, it was a partridge, or could it have been a cock pheasant or, confirming my worst fears, the limp, speckled form of Fairy Feet?

Safe And Sound

THIS afternoon there's a rainbow spanning Croft Douglas. It's unusual at the end of the year, but so welcome when the countryside needs a colourful cheering up. It's a supreme effort by a weakly sun to refract the light from the curtain of sleety rain that is being drawn across the hillside by the west wind that can blow hot and cold at a moment's notice.

Our children used to don their wet-weather clothes and dash out, often for more than a mile, to breathlessly dig for a fortune at the end of the coloured arc. That's probably why I find myself digging today.

I found an old horseshoe and carried it carefully home the right way up, so its legendary good luck wouldn't leak out.

When I reach the outbuildings there's a flurry of wings. It's Fairy Feet flying to meet me in her own inimitable way! She then leads me to the woodshed to show where she has been all day.

There, in a corner, is a fastidiously-fashioned nest of woodchips and wisps of hay and, lying like a precious jewel carefully laid in a bed of lambswool, is Fairy Feet's very first egg. □

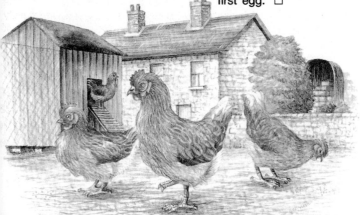

Through The

THE sun shines through the bedroom window on to the dressing-table mirror, and I catch my breath in horror at my reflection.

Unmistakably in the middle of my brown hair is a long, silver hair. Hastily I pull it out and examine it.

"There's no justice," I mutter. "I'm too young to go grey — only thirty-eight. Martin hasn't any grey hairs and he's two years older than me, but then of course his hair is much lighter than mine. Maybe they don't show up."

Gloom hangs over me as I finish making the beds. Finding that grey hair makes me realise that I'm not as young as I was — that forty is creeping up on me. I've been wondering what I'll do with myself now that Lynne is married, and Steven will soon be going to university. The house will be very empty without the children, and everything seems to be coming to an end.

I could always work full time instead of just mornings. They've asked me to often enough, but that would be a poor substitute for family life.

Suppose I were to have another baby, I ask myself. It would be like a new beginning.

I imagine telling Martin he's going to be a father again, and seeing him almost burst with pride.

It gives me a nice feeling to think of Martin. We've been right together ever since we first met — all those years ago.

I realise now that there are too many problems involved for me to have another baby at my age. I smile ruefully as I tell myself, "You can't win. You're either too young or too old."

I remember the first night I met Martin, at the youth club. dance. I was fifteen. I had known right away that he was the only one for me.

My parents thought me too young to have a steady boyfriend, and they had come to collect me after the dance, to give me a lift home. I had had to say goodbye to Martin with them sitting in the car — watching.

He used to meet me from school, first on his bicycle which he'd wheel home beside me. Later, when he was old enough, I would ride on the pillion of his motor bike, while all the young kids at school stared open mouthed.

When he did finally kiss me, in the little lane that was a short cut to my home, we clung together desperately, as though we were both afraid of being torn apart.

Looking Glass

Complete Story by DAPHNE RICHARDSON

**There it was — that single, heart-stopping grey hair
that made her take stock of her whole future . . .**

THROUGH THE LOOKING GLASS

"Let's go to Gretna Green and get married," I suggested, suddenly bold.

His fingers played with my pony tail, removing the elastic band and letting my long hair fall about my shoulders.

"We can't, Helen, they're not allowed to conduct weddings over the anvil any more. And, besides, how would we live? Once I'm a qualified draughtsman, and you're at training college, we'll get married. We've plenty of time, we've the whole future ahead of us."

Dear Martin, even at eighteen he was the sensible one, while I only knew what I wanted at the time.

We spent every spare moment together, even doing our homework in each other's house. Then on my eighteenth birthday, during my last year at school, we got engaged.

Martin bought the ring with the money he'd earned by doing a Saturday job. The rest of the week he was at the technical college, having nearly completed his studies.

When term started I was surrounded by a group of admiring girls, all gazing at the sparkling solitaire on my finger. Then the news reached the headmistress's ears and she told me off for wearing jewellery, so I kept it on a chain round my neck, under the blouse of my school uniform.

Finally both sets of parents relented and allowed us to get married the following Easter.

I shall never forget our wedding. The sun shone, and all our schoolfriends were there, while their parents tut-tutted and asked what our parents were thinking about, letting us get married so young.

MY wedding ring, surprisingly enough, was allowed at school, as I was leaving at the end of the summer term and starting at the teachers' training college.

Fate decided otherwise. I left school that summer, and when September came I discovered that I was pregnant.

Although it came as a surprise, it was a happy one. At first it was difficult to manage financially, so I got a job for six months.

Martin was earning good money by the time our daughter, Lynne, arrived. And by the time our son, Steven, was born, two years later, things were a lot easier.

It's strange how sure we were that our feelings for each other would never change — even when I was still only fifteen.

Lynne was just as sure when she met Alan, although she was seventeen by then. So we gladly gave our consent for her to be married two years later. Not that she needed it by then, but she still asked first, which made us very proud.

We've had a good marriage, Martin and I, and things are so much easier now, so why, I wonder, do I get a lump in my throat when I think of the girl and boy at the youth club dance, all those years ago?

I laugh aloud. "Do you know what started all this?" I ask Fred, our large tabby cat, as I finish tidying the bedrooms. "One grey hair, that's all," I tell him.

FRED looks at me indifferently, he really couldn't care less. But it's different for him — his whiskers are grey anyway!
I give in to impulse and pull open a drawer where I keep all the bits and pieces that are mementoes of our family life. There's an old diary from the early days of our marriage, a couple of pressed flowers from some forgotten occasion, school photos of Lynne and Steven . . .

I sit there, giving in to memories for a little while, then decide that I've enjoyed enough nostalgia for that day.

I make myself a snack lunch, then put Steven's football things to soak, shaking my head because he's left them on the floor, as usual. I am just about to get out the vacuum cleaner and start the usual boring housework, when the back door opens and Lynne bursts in.

I drop everything and put my arms round her — I'm so pleased and happy to see her.

"Oh, Lynne, what a lovely surprise!" I hug her until she's breathless, all blonde curls and apple cheeks. "Why aren't you at work, you're not ill, are you?" I ask, never having seen her look better.

She looks at me with Martin's blue eyes and long, dark lashes. "No, Mum. I'm fine — I've just come from the doctor's — I'm going to have a baby.

"I know we didn't plan on having one so soon, and I intended to go on working, but now that it's happened I'm so excited . . ."

No need to ask if she's happy about it, she looks radiant.

"And Alan?" I ask. "How does he feel about it?"

"He was a bit shattered at first, but now he's over the moon, even though money'll be a bit tight. We'll manage, though. After all, you and Dad did."

"I know just how you feel," I tell her. "I felt the same when I knew I was going to have you. A baby's more important than a job or career, any day."

I make some fresh coffee. "Or perhaps you'd rather have milk?" I ask anxiously.

Lynne laughs. "Not yet, Mum. I'll enjoy the coffee while I can."

"Is there anything I can make for the baby?" I ask anxiously as we drink our coffee, knowing I'm no good at sewing and could never make a christening gown.

She looks doubtful. "Do you remember that lovely cobwebby shawl you made for Steven years ago — the one I had later for my dolls? Do you think you could make me another one like it?"

"Of course, darling," I answer. "Do you feel like choosing the pattern and the wool on your way home, if I come with you? I've

Continued on page 87.

83

Party Pieces

Our pretty party mats are useful for any occasion — and they're so easy to knit in feather-stitch. Perfect, too, when you want to contribute to a fund-raising event.

Materials Required — Of **Coats Chain Mercer-Crochet Cotton No. 20,** 2 x 20-gram balls (this quantity will make 6 mats). One pair 2 mm (No. 14) Milward Disc knitting needles.

Quantities of yarn stated are based on average requirements and are therefore approximate.

For best results it is essential to use the recommended yarn. If you have difficulty in obtaining the yarn, write direct, enclosing a stamped, addressed envelope, to the following address for stockists: Consumer Services Department, Coats Patons Crafts, McMullen Road, Darlington, County Durham DL1 1YQ.

Measurements — About 16.5 centimetres, *6½ inches,* in diameter.

Tension — 44 stitches to 10 centimetres, *4 inches,* measured over garter-stitch edge.

If your tension is too tight, try a size larger needles. If it is too loose, try a size smaller.

Abbreviations — K — knit; P — purl; cm — centimetres; ins — inches; sts — stitches; tog — together; yfd — yarn forward.

TO MAKE

Cast on 250 sts. Work 4 rows garter-stitch (every row is a K row).

1st row — ★(K2 tog) 4 times, K1, (yfd, K1) 8 times, (K2 tog) 4 times, repeat from ★ to end.

2nd and every alternate row — P.

3rd row — ★(K3 tog) twice, K2 tog, K2, (yfd, K1) 5 times, yfd, K2, K2 tog, (K3 tog) twice, repeat from ★ to end.

5th row — ★(K2 tog) 3 times, K2, (yfd, K1) 5 times, yfd, K2, (K2 tog) 3 times, repeat from ★ to end.

7th row — ★(K3 tog) twice, K2 tog, (yfd, K1) 5 times, yfd, K2 tog, (K3 tog) twice, repeat from ★ to end.

9th row — ★(K2 tog) 3 times, (yfd, K1) 5 times, yfd, (K2 tog) 3 times, repeat from ★ to end.

11th row — ★K3 tog, K2 tog, K2, (yfd, K1) 3 times, yfd, K2, K2 tog, K3 tog, repeat from ★ to end.

13th row — ★(K2 tog) twice, K2, (yfd, K1) 3 times, yfd, K2, (K2 tog) twice, repeat from ★ to end.

15th row — ★K3 tog, K2 tog, K1, (yfd, K1) 4 times, K2 tog, K3 tog, repeat from ★ to end.

17th row — ★K3 tog, K2 tog, (yfd, K1) 3 times, yfd, K2 tog, K3 tog, repeat from ★ to end.

19th row — ★K3 tog, K2, yfd, K1, yfd, K2, K3 tog, repeat from ★ to end.

21st row — ★K3 tog, K1, (yfd, K1) twice, K3 tog, repeat from ★ to end.

23rd row — ★K3 tog, yfd, K1, yfd, K3 tog, repeat from ★ to end.

25th row — ★K2 tog, yfd, K1, yfd, K2 tog, repeat from ★ to end.

27th row — ★K2 tog, K1, K2 tog, repeat from ★ to end.

29th row — ★K3 tog, repeat from ★ to end — 10 sts.

30th row — P.

Cut thread, leaving about 30 cm, 11¾ ins. Thread through remaining sts, draw up centre, fasten securely, then neatly join seam. Damp and pin out to given measurement. ∎

some shopping I'd like to do this morning."

I hadn't realised till then that I'd need anything, as Steven's going to a friend's for the evening, and there will only be Martin and me.

Now I'm determined to get something special for Martin's evening meal. Perhaps a mixed grill, that's his favourite. It's not every day I have news like this to tell him.

Lynne and I catch the bus, an easy thing to do at this hour of the day, unlike the morning rush hour. In a few minutes we're in the shop looking at patterns and delicate machine-washable baby wool.

She chooses one as near to the original shawl as we can remember, and we walk out proudly with our purchase. After kissing her, she goes one way and I go the other — in the direction of the butcher's.

Home once more, I put the wool away in a safe place, and start preparing the supper.

I TAKE great pains with the meal. Then, just before Martin is due home, I slip up and change my dress, undo my hair from its french pleat and brush it out round my shoulders. For once I'm pleased with my appearance.

Martin comes in, takes one look at me and whistles! I carry the meal through to the carefully-laid candle-lit table.

"What did I do to deserve this?" he asks, smiling up at me like a small boy.

"I'll tell you later, after we've eaten," I say teasingly.

Later, when he pushes his empty plate away and gives a sigh of contentment, I say softly:

"Lynne's going to have a baby."

He stares at me blankly. "But she's only been married five months, and what about her job? And the money they were going to put by first?"

I laugh at him. "You sound just like my dad did all those years ago. They'll manage all right — after all, we did."

"Yes," he says slowly, "and we were even younger."

Then he gives me a long look and says almost shyly, "Helen, you should always wear your hair down. You look just like you did the first night I met you at the youth club, and you were only fifteen, remember?"

Suddenly I feel choked, because I realise he is remembering, just as I did, the girl and boy that used to be. The young couple that turned into us, Martin and me.

"You don't mind being married to a grandmother?" I ask, my voice shaking a little.

"Not one as young and lovely as you," he says, then adds with a grin, "but being a grandfather does make me feel *old*!"

We both laugh then, and he gets up from the table and kisses me. It's then I realise that life for me is anything but over, in spite of that first grey hair. In fact, it's only just beginning — all over again! □

**She gave the child a beautiful present —
but it was nothing compared to the gift she received
in return.**

SUGAR
and
SPICE

Complete Story by FRANCES FITZGIBBON

IT was finished at last! I stood back and surveyed my masterpiece. It was no oil painting — no contemplative creation from alabaster or clay — not even one of my forlorn attempts at dressmaking.

What stood before me was a fairy castle in a delicate shade of pink, its ethereal image reflected in the lake upon which it stood. Lacy doyleys formed the pinnacles rising majestically from its four corner turrets, and a wall of sugar lumps surrounded it.

In the centre of the castle rested a miniature tinfoil crown, and I was still pondering where I would place the seven pink candles.

The birthday cake had taken me all afternoon and my back still ached from piping the tiny pink stars round every edge, but I wouldn't have cared if it had taken me for ever, so long as it pleased my stepdaughter Katie.

Gilbert had promised to be back from his business trip early in the afternoon, and would bring some flashbulbs, so we'd have photos of the occasion for our new family album.

Katie didn't want friends invited, like the boys did on their birthdays; so there would just be the family.

That had worried me at first. I had wanted to make this first birthday with me a special occasion, but Gilbert had said not to press her, there would be other birthdays.

The front door opened, and a cheery, "Hello, Mum," from my elder son was all the excuse I needed to stop what I was doing.

"Hello!" I called. "I'm in the kitchen." I just had time to put the cake away before the boys came through.

"The photo's come." Tony clattered in and handed over a large envelope. "Malcolm's tie was crooked and his hair needed brushing."

"Didn't," retaliated Malcolm, his junior by a year. "And don't be so nosey."

"Now, you two, don't start straightaway. Where's Katie?" I looked towards the open kitchen door.

"I don't know." Malcolm shrugged.

"She went straight upstairs." Tony was sniffing round the large baking bowl. "Mmm. They for tea, Mum?"

"Come away, Tony." I crossed to the hall. "Katie! You all right, love?"

"Yes," came the quiet reply.

I tried again. "Tony's brought the school photo. Come and see."

No answer. Suppressing a longing to go up to her, I went back into the kitchen and took out the photo.

"Oh! That's lovely." I held the print at a distance, and Malcolm, coming to look, sniggered.

"Tony looks like a girl with his hair like that."

"It's a jolly good photo of all three of you." I ignored their bantering.

"Katie's not smiling," Malcolm pointed out.

"Still, it's like her." Tony stood beside me, an arm through mine.

At that moment Katie appeared in the doorway.

"Has anyone seen Heidi?" Her large blue eyes were moist and there was a catch in her small voice.

Please don't let her cry, I willed. Not in front of the boys. That had happened too often since Gilbert and I had married.

MY pair of toughs had accepted him quite happily, and were ready to accept his daughter, too. But for Katie, our marriage had been a blow, and the boys' teasing didn't help.

"Who wants soppy baby dolls, anyway?" Malcolm scoffed.

"Heidi's as old as me," Katie said. "How can she be a baby?"

"Upstairs!" I interrupted, steering Malcolm to the doorway. "You, too, Tony. Get changed before tea.

"Now, Katie, what's this about Heidi?" I sat down at the table and looked fondly at the small girl, her pretty dark hair falling in a shower about her round face, so like Gilbert's.

"She doesn't seem to be where I left her." The child's voice was far too controlled for a seven-year-old.

"She can't be far away." I remembered with a sinking feeling that Skipper had been in her room sometime today. Hadn't I found the dog's old, chewed-up slipper abandoned on her floor among scattered toys which Heidi usually set carefully in their place?

"Heidi'll turn up," I said with more assurance than I felt. "Come and sit here." I made room for Katie on the chair. "Let's look at this lovely photo of you and the boys."

Katie moved towards me, but didn't sit down. She stood there, her arms folded, looking at the photograph.

"Yes. It's quite good. Last time, I had one taken on my own."

"That's right — the one we have on top of the television. Perhaps we'll swap them over, but we'll keep this clean until Daddy's seen it." I replaced the photo and put it to one side.

"He said he'd be back for my birthday — that's tomorrow. Maybe he'll know where Heidi is."

She seemed more settled after that, and didn't mention her doll again that evening.

A T bedtime, Katie gave me the customary peck on the cheek. With her soap-scented body so close, I wanted to hug her to me, but remembering that last time when she'd frozen rigid in my arms, I resisted the temptation.

Girls were different from boys. Hadn't all my friends tried to tell me that when I married Gilbert? Moody, unpredictable, precocious — I should expect a stepdaughter to be all these things and more besides.

Perhaps I was rushing things, wanting to run before I could walk, expecting miracles? But not really. I just wanted some small sign, something to give me hope that, in the future, things would one day be good between us.

So far the only cross words Gil and I had had were over Katie.

"Consult a child psychiatrist? Don't be ridiculous! Some kids are simply more affectionate than others." Gil had looked at me, and his eyes had softened. "Besides, give her time. Look at the boys — they never leave *me* alone!"

That was just the problem — Gil had never really had to try. My sons had called him Dad almost from the beginning, though I have to admit we'd rehearsed it. How could Gilbert know what I was going through?

Long after he should have been asleep that night, Tony crept downstairs.

"What do you think, Mum? Do you think she'll like it?"

Opening his dressing-gown, he held the missing doll up for my inspection.

I recognised Heidi from the familiar rouged cheeks, and rosebud lips and the brown pigtails. But her faded cotton dress had been replaced by a pale blue shirt and darker blue dungarees.

"Tony! However . . . ?"

"One of the girls in my class gave me them. Do you think she'll like it? Katie, I mean? It's a sort of surprise for her birthday. It only cost me half a bag of conkers."

I looked at his anxious face, and swallowed. "Of course she

Continued on page 98.

91

Topsy-Turvy

He was a knight in distress, then along came a damsel in shining armour! (Well, we told you it was topsy-turvy, didn't we?)

GRAHAM DAVIS stood at the window and looked out at the city. It was dusk and lights were beginning to go on all around him, some near, some so far they seemed almost like stars.

The sight had always given him a feeling of excitement, tonight more than ever. For tonight he was standing at his *own* window — in his *own* flat.

He heaved a sigh of relief — no more room-mates, no more landladies urging him to write to his mother. From now on he was going to lead the life of a man-about-town.

There would be small gatherings of friends — he pictured them standing by his window, sipping drinks, indulging in sophisticated conversation — and intimate dinner parties for two, with superb steaks from his kitchen and wines he spoke about knowledgeably . . .

The excitement died inside him, leaving him dull and empty. As empty, he thought, as the flat around him.

It was no use kidding himself that a boiling ring and a bed were all he needed. Chairs and a table were also fairly essential — not to mention a carpet to cover those awful floorboards and a lamp to read by.

Kind Of Love

Complete Story

by PAMELA SPECK

As for the friends who were going to sip drinks and sparkle by his window — he'd been so busy learning his new job, since he'd come to the city, that he hadn't really had time to acquire many of those.

He certainly hadn't met anyone with whom to share an intimate dinner party. Come to think of it, he didn't even know very much about wine.

But Graham was a cheerful sort, not easily discouraged. A bite of food was all he needed, he told himself. With something solid inside his stomach, life — and the flat — would seem less bleak.

So he cooked himself some bacon and eggs and sat by his window, taking a look at his neighbours while he ate.

There wasn't much to see, as most people had already drawn their curtains; but there were some, he was happy to note, who were just like him — they didn't have any curtains to draw.

The flat opposite was in darkness, but the one below it was brightly lit and, looking down, he had a perfect view of the sitting-room.

It was strange, he thought, how some people — like himself — always started out with the odds against them. He had only his skill and ingenuity to fill his flat. Yet there were others, like that girl down there, who had everything going for them.

He noted enviously the shining expanse of polished floor, the large, bright cushions that served as chairs. The colourful splash the bookcase made against the wall — the bookcase itself, rigged up out of planks and builder's bricks.

Then Graham came to a halt in his inventory-taking — it had suddenly dawned on him that the flat he was looking at had as little real furniture as his own, yet somehow it managed to look like an illustration from a magazine.

He took another look at the girl. She was pale, with mousy brown hair — not the sort of girl he normally looked at twice. Well, he decided, if Miss Mouse could do it, so could he.

Over the following days he studied her flat carefully. The shining floor was obviously the work of a sanding machine — and much better than a carpet, he decided, when he'd finished sanding his.

The cushions came from a shop around the corner and the bookshelves were easy.

His flat, he saw with satisfaction, was beginning to look almost as bright as Miss Mouse's. She was a clever girl — what a pity she didn't apply some of that decorating flair to herself. Because if anybody needed a bright coat of paint and a bit of shine, she did . . .

Then, one evening, something happened that put Miss Mouse and her interior decorating right out of his mind.

There was a swish of distant curtains, a sudden blaze of light — and the flat opposite, which had been deserted and in darkness ever since he'd moved in, came to instant, vivid life!

A girl danced on to the balcony — a mind-boggling, eye-popping miracle of a girl. Her hair aflame in the sunset, she spread out long, luscious arms to the city below and called out what sounded like, "Hello, there — I'm back!"

Back from a long holiday abroad, Graham guessed, judging by her tan.

He had a fierce urge to lean out and call back, "Hello, there — I'm *here!*" But he couldn't.

He wasn't the kind of chap who did that sort of thing . . . How he wished he was!

HE watched her, almost permanently open mouthed, for the next few evenings. He'd never seen anyone like her in his life.

Her flat reflected her personality, he thought — it blazed, like her delightful hair, and seemed to have all that the consumer society ordained a girl like her should have.

Graham knew that he must meet her.

But how — ? There wouldn't be any problem about *that,* surely? Men were meeting girls all the time. On buses, on tubes, even in taxis . . .

He could lurk near the entrance to the flats on a rainy day, holding an umbrella. Or pretend to be a delivery man and take her some flowers . . .

"Why not just phone her up and ask for a date?" someone in the office suggested wearily.

That would have been simple if Graham had known her telephone number. But he didn't even know her name. Then he brightened — he might not have her number but he had an idea.

Graham bought some whitewash at a paint shop that evening. Then he went straight home, stood in front of his window and prayed. It had to work — she *had* to get the message. He didn't see how anyone could possibly fail to . . .

SLOWLY, carefully, he painted his telephone number on the window in huge white letters. She was bound to see it, he kept telling himself. All he had to do now was sit back and wait for his phone to ring . . .

He didn't have long to wait. Her voice, when he heard it, sounded exactly as he knew it would. Like the chime of temple bells. And he knew that he'd be quite happy to listen to it for the rest of his life.

Admittedly, her words weren't quite what he'd hoped for, but they would do for a start.

"Are you ill?" she asked. "Housebound? In some sort of trouble? Or are you just a new kind of telephone freak?"

Graham was horrified. Of course. Why hadn't he realised — ? Girls just didn't ring up men who wrote their telephone numbers on windows. He had to have a good story.

Although her words weren't exactly cordial, there was something in her voice that gave him hope. It sounded like the voice of someone he could talk to . . .

There were all sorts of things Graham would have liked to tell her. About the home he'd left, his friends, his schooldays even . . . He would have liked to begin at the beginning and go on and on.

A girl with a voice like that was the sort who would listen, comment and laugh in the right places.

Then he would have said, "Now, *you* tell me about yourself." And they would have found out they had just about everything in common.

But that was the way you talked to a girl you knew better than anyone else — and this was a girl he didn't know at all.

So, instead, he started by telling her his name and how he'd just come to the city. Somehow the loneliness he'd met there seemed to creep in, too.

He also told her about his empty flat, his equally empty pocket, and his singular lack of bright ideas about these problems.

She was every bit as understanding as he'd known she would be.

"I think it would be a good idea to concentrate on your flat first," she said thoughtfully. "Loneliness is much easier to bear in a cheerful place, I think."

She paused. "And let's face it, Graham, finding friends is not the sort of thing you do in a hurry. I'm sure you'll agree that as we get older we get so much more *discriminating.*"

Graham couldn't believe his luck. She wasn't just wonderful, she was wise as well — and obviously *very* discriminating.

His proposal that they should meet on neutral territory got no response. Instead she promised to think up some cheap and cheerful ideas for his flat and suggested he call her later in the week. She gave him her phone number.

When Graham hung up he felt dazed, but happy.

Later, he spotted her on the balcony, a vivid figure in the dusk, and rushed to his window to wave enthusiastically. She waved back and in the falling darkness it seemed she blew him the lightest of kisses. He was ecstatic.

They talked again and again. It was odd, he thought, how with her, one topic led on so easily to another without any awkward pauses. How much more interesting everything became when he discussed it with her. How his flat had taken shape and magically become home under her guidance.

Strange that someone who had never even seen the place could have made such a difference to it.

Weeks had gone by and Graham hadn't been able to persuade her to go out with him. He'd never seen anyone like her before, had never spoken to anyone at such length about so many things. Yet they remained just telephone friends.

There was always something else she had to do — like taking magazines to Mrs Somebody who was in hospital. Fixing supper for Mrs S.'s three children . . .

Graham didn't believe a word of it. A girl who looked like that must have hordes of men battling for the privilege of taking her out in their fast cars and buying her expensive meals.

But he was thankful for whatever crumbs fell from her table, for she was never too busy to talk with him. And whenever she was on her balcony, she turned that bright, delightful head and blew him those light kisses . . .

It was one of those wind-blown kisses that spurred Graham into action. He got home one evening to see her watering the potted plants, her dress showing off pale golden shoulders, her hair like a jewel in the sun.

She turned, aware of him, and put the watering-can down. Then, quite deliberately, she threw him a long, slow kiss with both hands. She paused just long enough to see the effect it had on him, then turned back to her potted plants with a smile.

GRAHAM went straight to the phone. "Look, we can't go on not meeting like this!"

She laughed. "Why, what would you rather we did?"

"I'd rather you came over and actually saw what wonders you've done to my flat instead of talking about them on the phone. Then, I think it would be a very good idea if you let me take you out for a meal. I know a place where we can get excellent pizzas and a very palatable plonk."

Graham held his breath and waited. The lady might be home from hospital, the three children might have had their supper — but there was sure to be something else. There always was.

She said softly, "Thank you. I'm very fond of pizzas and I'd love to see the flat. I'll be over in about an hour."

The doorbell rang just over an hour later. Graham got to the door with long, swift strides, threw it open eagerly — then stood quite still. He looked at the girl who stood there and she looked at him.

All sorts of thoughts raced through his mind. Thoughts like — so this is the girl I've been baring my soul to all these weeks — this is the girl who turned my flat into my home. But where on earth have I seen her before?

For she was small and pale and her hair was quite an ordinary shade of brown — some might have called it mousy.

Then Graham remembered. He'd seen her that first week he moved in. He'd copied the ideas in her flat so carefully — the sanding machine, the bookcase. She was Miss Mouse.

She had no halo of bright hair, no tanned arms that threw kisses across the road to men she didn't know. She had, instead, the loveliest smile he had ever seen and a voice like — well, like temple chimes.

"Hello, Graham," she said, smiling. "Aren't you going to ask me in?"

There was no doubt at all in his mind — it was the sort of voice he could listen to for the rest of his life.

He beamed at her. "Come in, come in!" □

will, son. Here, let me see." I put my hands out for the doll. "There's some wrapping paper in that cupboard if you want to . . ."

"Oh, no. I'll just put it back in her room so she'll see it when she wakes up."

I thought of the pink party dress for Katie, wrapped up in a fancy box. I thought of the fairy castle, iced in pink and adorned with silver flags. And I wondered where I was going wrong.

Here was this sensitive child of mine, who'd brought tears to my eyes and would bring joy to Katie by this simple, but so thoughtful gift . . .

Next morning, Katie eyed the fancy box without enthusiasm, and opened it when she was invited to.

"Thank you. It's lovely," was her polite, correct response.

"Wouldn't you like to try it on, dear? You've time before school." My words hung heavy in the silence. Where was the light in her eyes that I'd so hoped to see?

"I'll wait . . . till Daddy's here, if you don't mind." She glanced doubtfully at me. "But can I take Heidi to school? Look what Tony's done!"

For the first time there was some warmth in her voice as she held the doll proudly out to me.

For the first time in my life I felt a pang of jealousy towards my own son. I'd had visions of Katie gasping with delight when she saw that dress, flinging her arms round my neck. How could such a small child be so cool, so self-possessed?

By mid-afternoon, the house was quiet about me. The castle cake was in its place in the centre of the table, and next to it a plate of gingerbread men watched me with their currant eyes and angelica smiles.

I was putting sausages on sticks when the telephone rang.

It was Miss Wood, Katie's teacher.

"Miss Wood! What is it! Has something happened to Katie?" Panic was rising in my throat.

"No. Nothing like that, Mrs Graham. She's a lovely child. But I just thought . . ."

"What is it then?" What was she taking so long to tell me?

"Well, there *has* been a little upset, but she's all right now. You see, we have a student in this week. Perhaps Katie's told you?"

"No. I don't think she did." Miss Wood knew how things were between Katie and me.

"Well . . . It seems the student was reading them a story about a wicked stepmother . . ."

A WAVE of nausea swept over me as I clutched the phone, waiting, yet afraid of hearing more.

"Go on," I heard myself say.

"Well, Katie ran from the classroom sobbing and came to find me. Now don't worry, Mrs Graham — I thought that, too, for a moment. But it's all right, really. Katie was annoyed, upset. She said it was a lie — people shouldn't write bad stories like that."

"She said that?" My head began to clear, and a warm feeling enveloped me.

"Not only that!" Miss Wood sounded elated. "Katie went back into that classroom with me, and told her class she knew about stepmothers. They weren't cruel like the story said, but just ordinary, like real mothers."

I gasped, and Miss Wood added, "Those were her own words."

A small bubble of happiness swelled inside me, but Miss Wood was still talking.

"I know it's Katie's birthday today. Of course, she doesn't know I'm phoning you, but . . . well, I wondered if you just might be here to meet her when she comes out of school. As a sort of treat?"

Did it matter that the sausages weren't on sticks yet? Did it matter that I hadn't put the candles on the cake? Suddenly I wanted to sing.

"That's a lovely idea, Miss Wood."

Just then the front door opened, and Gilbert, his dark hair tousled by the wind, grinned a welcome. I held out a hand to him.

He put his arms round me and began whispering endearments, so that I couldn't concentrate on what Miss Wood was saying.

"I'll tell her you'll be there, shall I?"

"No! No, please don't do that, Miss Wood." I fended Gilbert off with one hand. "We'll let it be a surprise — but her father and I will both come down to meet her."

"That's wonderful — thank you, Mrs Graham." The teacher rang off, and I turned to face my husband's questioning eyes.

"What was all that about?"

"Nothing, love. Come on — we're going to meet the kids coming out of school."

Such an ordinary phrase — such an ordinary thing to do. But blazoned before me on a golden banner were Katie's words — "Ordinary, like a real mother." And they made this particular day the happiest of my life. □

© Frances Fitzgibbon 1979.

ORIENTAL BEAUTY

She was blue eyed and slinky, and completely indifferent to the small boy eating his heart out for her.

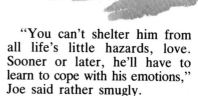

UNREQUITED love is seldom painless. For Ben Howard, not quite five years old, it was unbearable. He was madly in love with Yod Rak, a Siamese cat which refused to have anything to do with him.

His mother, Sally, realised what Ben was going through, but there was little she could do to help him.

"I feel so sorry for him," she said to her husband, Joe, as she prepared the evening meal. "If I'd foreseen this kind of situation, I wouldn't have agreed to take Yod Rak when the Wilsons decided to emigrate to Australia."

"You can't shelter him from all life's little hazards, love. Sooner or later, he'll have to learn to cope with his emotions," Joe said rather smugly.

Yod Rak adored Joe. He was the one member of the household to whom she had given unqualified approval. His return from the office was greeted with great enthusiasm, and she monopolised him from the moment he entered the front door.

"Then let it be sooner rather than later!" Sally set the salad bowl on the table. "I can't stand the strain much longer. It's heartbreaking to watch his futile efforts to make friends."

"The Wilson boys are probably responsible for her attitude. I expect they've left her with a permanent distrust of small boys. Those little thugs were enough to scare the living daylights out of anyone," Joe said, grinning.

"Could be. They used to tease her mercilessly. I'd made up my mind to threaten them with the R.S.P.C.A., then Jean came up with what seemed the ideal solution!"

"And so it will be, love. Give her time to settle down. You'll see . . ."

"Let's hope you're right. I was so thrilled that Jean wanted me to have Yod Rak. Surely the wretched animal can see Ben's different? She's not stupid."

"Far from it!" Joe agreed, as the new member of their family leapt on his lap, and examined his supper critically, as if to ensure that Joe was receiving proper treatment.

Had she not immediately recognised him as a superior being? Her adoration boosted his ego no end.

But mothers share their children's trials and woes. When Yod Rak pointedly walked away, waving her tail angrily because Ben had tried to stroke her, the unfriendliness wounded Sally, too.

"She's all right with me," she said, defensively. "Yesterday, I was weeding the garden and she leapt on to my shoulder and curled her paws around my neck."

THE honour had gone to Sally's head. Flushed with triumph at this mark of favour, she had carried Yod Rak indoors, convinced her wishes would be respected.

Ben was watching "Blue Peter". He grinned delightedly when she dumped his beloved on to his lap. But even the television, which Yod Rak usually enjoyed, did not overcome Yod Rak's dislike of little boys.

Before Ben could lift his hand to stroke her creamy flank, she had taken refuge on top of the bookcase. She crouched there, her blue eyes glaring down at them.

Sally tried bribery. She got Ben to feed Yod Rak. But luscious pieces of expensive fish and fresh cream did not soften her. A cat of Yod Rak's moral stature can't be bought.

Sally tried subtle tricks . . . closing the door, and leaving the unhappy couple alone together. But the minute she returned, Yod Rak shot from the room like a cheetah released from a trap.

"If only Ben wasn't so crazy about cats, the situation might be easier." Sally sighed.

Since babyhood he had adored them, often leaning from his pram to stroke some scruffy stray. Once he had learned to talk, he nagged constantly for a kitten of his own.

Time and again, Sally had been about to get him one when some domestic crisis had intervened. The Wilsons' departure for Australia had seemed the answer to a prayer.

"Perhaps if we got a companion for her," Sally suggested to Joe one evening, "a common, cross-bred puss, Ben would transfer his affections."

Joe agreed that the idea might work, but when Sally suggested it to Ben he gazed at her sadly. He knew there would only ever be one cat for him.

"They'd be company for each other," she added lamely, but Ben turned away and tried to interest his cruel lady in a length of bright-green wool.

"Yod Rak doesn't want company," he said firmly. "She just wants us."

At that, the subject of the discussion disappeared behind the couch. Correction, Sally thought. All she wants is a comfortable home, devoted slaves and your father!

For the moment she abandoned the hopeless struggle.

But troubles don't go away because you turn your back on them, and Ben continued to mope around the house.

"Send him to play school," Granny said briskly. "That'll take him out of himself."

"Oh, really Mother, isn't that a bit drastic? Why should our lives be completely disrupted just because of a temperamental Siamese cat?"

"It seems to me that's already happened!" Mrs Bartlett remarked. "She's taken over."

Yod Rak yawned, eyeing the visitor with mild disapproval, and running a lethal claw down her best tights.

"Put her in a cats' home for a week," Sally's next-door neighbour, Rita, advised. "After, she'll be so relieved to get back to you, she'll welcome any little kindness."

"Ben would be furious . . . and Joe wouldn't allow it. Anyway, I couldn't be so unfeeling. She's disturbed enough already, after being torn from her old surroundings."

"Well, if that's how you feel, don't ask my advice." Plainly, Rita had no patience with sentimentalists. "I wouldn't make myself a nervous wreck over an animal. She'd do as she was told or go . . . it's as simple as that."

Useless to point out that, if Yod Rak went, Ben would be terribly upset.

YOD RAK had been with the Howards for just over two weeks now, and the problem was as bad as ever.

Quiet and depressed because Yod Rak had once again vanished at the sight of him, Ben was "helping" to wash up the breakfast dishes. Giving his mother a hand with the chores helped to take his mind off the cat.

"I'm just going upstairs to make the beds," Sally said, switching on the tumble-drier as she left the kitchen.

She had just reached the landing when a cry of alarm halted her.

"Mummy, Mummy, come quick! The tumble-drier's making a funny noise. I think it's broken."

Prepared for an explosion, Sally raced downstairs. With commendable presence of mind, Ben had switched off the machine, and silence now reigned.

"What kind of noise was it, Ben? What a clever boy to switch off immediately. Keep back, and I'll take a look before I ring for a repair man."

"There was a funny squeaking, and lots of bumping about . . . as if it had a brick in it."

Continued on page 107

I USED to think that one never knew when a child might come down with a sudden illness, that there was no way to anticipate the sudden onset of a cold or fever. But out of the blue, I had a revelation. My children's illnesses *do* have a recognisable pattern.

As a simple example, my son can play for hours without getting a scratch on him. And the chances are that he will probably stay unscratched, unless, by chance, I get a long-distance telephone call. As soon as the call comes, as soon as I begin a conversation with a chum I haven't seen in ten years, in walks my son with a pained expression on his face.

"Mum, I fell down and scratched my knee. It hurts!"

Then there are the times when I decide to try out a delicious new recipe. While I am keeping an eye on the mixer as it slowly turns at the "fold" speed and while I slowly stir other ingredients in a saucepan at the same time, I can hear the wail.

"My chin! My chin!"

Only during special recipes do chins need stitches!

But these are spur-of-the-moment happenings which can be straightened out fairly quickly. The long-range illnesses are usually the outcome of a little more "planning."

BY A STRANGE

Have you ever made plans and just as you're on the point of carrying them out in steps Dame Misfortune

For example, the Sunday newspapers help me to arrange my weekly activities.

I read that the following week the big department store in town is holding a gigantic clearance sale, with every item in the store reduced. Doors will open one hour earlier and close two hours later so that everyone will have a chance to shop.

"Wow!" I say to myself as I check my purse, figure out what's in my bank account and make sure my credit cards are in my bag. Then I head for the phone.

"Hello, Marge, did you see the sale ad. in this morning's paper?"

Since Marge has just finished checking *her* purse, figuring out what's in *her* account and rounding up *her* credit cards, we make arrangements to spend the following Thursday at the sale.

During the week, I make a careful list of all the things I need and want that I could never afford at recommended prices — a new tablecloth, some kitchen curtains, a new jacket, underwear for the kids, etc.

Thursday morning I wake up, prepare to tidy the house as quickly as possible so that I can get out early, and what do I hear? Cough, cough!

"Mum," a weak voice calls from the children's bedroom. "I think I have flu." Nothing like a giant sale to create a case of flu!

MUCH as I love my children's company, it is a nice change to get away for a quiet weekend without them. In order to get away, however, I spend many hours of careful preparation. First, I check my wardrobe and my husband's. Do we have enough dressy clothes to last a weekend? The answer is usually "no," so I have to devote a week to shopping for clothing.

Next I have to see that the children will be properly taken care of.

"Lesley," I say, "I know Cindy has been wanting to stay with you. Why don't you ask her if she'd like to spend the weekend with you — at her house?" I have a list of substitutes if Cindy doesn't work!

Or, "Ricky, your friend David has just got a new Motorcycle Race game. Why don't you see if his mother will let you spend the weekend playing there, and, if you like the game, maybe we can get one for you?"

Here we can substitute Steven, Norman or Joe for David, and we

COINCIDENCE...

By
RONI
BORDEN

BY A STRANGE COINCIDENCE...

can always give the host youngster a Motorcycle Race game if he doesn't already have one.

If none of this works, I can always call up some neighbours and beg . . .

I then have to see that all the ironing in the house gets done the day before I am to leave. This guarantees that my children will not only have decent clothes to wear all weekend, but that they will have clean clothes to wear to school on Monday.

Finally, I have to do a little grocery shopping to make sure that there is enough food in the house to get us through breakfast on Monday morning.

I must repeat — this takes hours of preparation. But all the effort is worth it. That is, it would be worth it if I really got to leave, but usually the morning of the big weekend I hear so much coughing and sneezing coming from at least one of my children, that I know for certain that my children will be allowed nowhere at all except in their own beds.

NOW that I know how illnesses start, I make it a point to buy tickets only for bad plays. The one time I planned to see a play that really interested me, I had to buy the ticket several months in advance. Naturally, on the night of the performance, my youngest developed an earache that could only be soothed by my presence.

And, of course, inviting company more than ten minutes in advance is always a calculated risk.

Whenever I invite someone I really want to spend a long evening with, and after I spend several days cleaning the house, spend hours with a recipe book musing over recipes for hors d'oeuvres, and spend half my grocery budget on expensive wine, the company shows up and do you know who I spend the evening with? With one of my children, naturally, trying to relieve the pain of a sore throat!

If all this sounds as though my children are frequently ill, let me assure you that they are not. I have a sure-fire method of keeping them exceedingly healthy.

All I have to do is plan a household job that I really hate doing, such as cleaning out the cupboards, or letting down the hems of last year's jeans and, much as I try and try, I can't unearth even a single sniffle as an excuse to dodge the chore. □

Ignoring her warning, Ben opened the door to reveal the familiar jumble of sheets and towels.

But not only the week's laundry flopped out on to the floor. From under the washing, a nightmare figure emerged. Bleary eyed and dazed, Yod Rak tottered from her ill-chosen hide-out, a very bemused cat.

SICK with apprehension, Sally bent to pick Yod Rak up, but Ben forestalled her. Cradling the limp body in his arms, he spoke softly to the cat. Too weak to resist, Yod Rak lay there, accepting his caress.

"It was absolutely shattering," Sally said later, describing the incident to Joe. "He thought she was done for . . . and she would have been, if Ben hadn't realised something was wrong.

"Normally I leave the tumble-drier to complete its cycle, while I get on with the rest of the work. She could have been there for ages."

"I wondered why she didn't come down the path to meet me. Is she still groggy?"

"Not in the least. Within ten minutes she was stalking a beetle across the lawn, as though nothing had happened."

"What a disaster!" Joe suddenly dissolved into roars of laughter. "Wait till I tell the lads in the office! They'll be falling about over this. What a crazy thing to do."

"It wasn't funny!" Sally protested but his merriment was infectious. After all, Yod Rak had survived the ordeal, and laughter was as good a way as any to express relief.

"Well, there goes the first of her nine lives . . . "

"And I have to admit it had a happy ending," Sally said.

"Yes, indeed, since she's back to normal."

"Oh, more than that, Joe. Wait until you see what I mean."

Joe, still dabbing his eyes to remove the tears of laughter, looked puzzled as she led him upstairs.

"What do you think of that?" she asked, pushing open Ben's bedroom door.

The evening sun shone through the closed curtains. Surrounded by books, crayons, a moth-eaten teddy bear, and the bedraggled scrap of blanket he called his Moulie, Ben slept peacefully. And at his feet, on the gold patch of sunlight, purring like a steam engine, lay Yod Rak.

"She's scarcely left his side all day," Sally whispered. "That's why she didn't come to meet you. You've got a rival for his affections now. Do you think you can take it like a man!"

"I'll do my best to keep a stiff upper lip," Joe said, planting a kiss on his son's forehead.

Two bright blue eyes watched him keenly, as Yod Rak assured herself that he meant no harm towards her hero. □

Everything

. . . was lovely until Albert started scheming to get his green fingers on next door's garden as well.

"AND about time, too!" Albert Douglas muttered, as he heard the door of the adjoining house bang.

He went to the kitchen window and peered out anxiously into the next-door garden.

Yes, there she was, making her way down the path to her drying green. He had begun to think that dratted woman wasn't going to show face all day.

Snatching up the daffodils he'd picked earlier that morning, and the best spring cabbage from his small vegetable plot, Albert hurried out to greet her.

Really, it had been a shame to pick those beautiful flowers, he thought. A crime against nature, almost. Still, it would be worth it if everything went according to plan. And worth all the other flowers and vegetables he'd showered on that Kitty

In The Garden

Complete
Story
by
SARAH
BURKHILL

Black since she had moved in last month.

Albert had been unable to believe his luck when the council allocated the end house to a widow. What would a woman living alone possibly want with all that garden? She could never cope with it, not in a million years!

He, on the other hand, with his already-overcrowded patch, could put some extra ground to good use. It was the perfect solution to both their problems — if the woman could just be made to see that, and persuaded to hand over her garden without a fuss.

"'Morning, Mrs Black!" he called brightly, ambling over to the fence that separated them. "Looks like you've picked a good drying day. Nice breeze coming up.

"Mind you," he went on, as she took a clothes peg out of her mouth, "it wouldn't have done these much good."

EVERYTHING IN THE GARDEN

He produced the bunch of daffodils from behind his back. "I thought you might like to have them, save them getting battered about outside."

Kitty Black beamed. "Why, they're beautiful! Are you sure? I mean, do you really want me to have them?"

"Couldn't think of a better home for them," Albert said ingratiatingly. He held up the spring cabbage. "And for this, too."

Kitty took the proffered gifts and he airily waved away her thanks.

"Not at all. Glad to be of some use to you." He shuffled nearer to the fence and leaned over. "And how are you settling in now?" he asked solicitously.

"All the better for your help," Kitty replied. "Really, I can't believe my good fortune in having a neighbour like you, Mr Douglas. You've been wonderful!"

Albert coughed, and assumed his most modest expression.

"Well, what are neighbours for?" he asked. "And anyway, I think we've become rather more than just neighbours, don't you? I hope you think of me as a — as a *friend,* too?"

"Oh, but I do, Mr Douglas," she assured him, eyes wide. "I most certainly do!"

Albert was silent for a moment. This was all very well, but how was he going to get round to the important matter of her ground? It seemed a trifle crude just to come out and say: "How's about giving me your garden?"

No, the question would have to be approached with great delicacy and tact, two qualities Albert prided himself on possessing in quantity.

"I expect you find it difficult managing on your own — what with having no man about," he said diffidently. "It's a pity you've got the end house, it being bigger and having so much more ground."

"Well, it's not always easy." Kitty sighed. "But I expect I shall cope. We have to cope, don't we?"

Albert tutted. "Mrs Black, I would hate to think of a lady like you having any difficulties. Not when I'm here and could — well, could make life so much easier for you, if you'd let me."

"Mr Douglas, how very gallant!" she simpered prettily, turning a delicate shade of pink. "I — I really don't know what to say."

Albert smiled back at her. Yes, it was all going very nicely. He couldn't have handled it better. In fact, he might not even have to throw in the offer of half the garden's produce, which he'd been keeping as a last resort should she prove difficult.

"Well, it would be to our mutual advantage, wouldn't it?" he said. "Since I retired I haven't had much to do except potter about in the garden all day. And of course you would have a much better outlook with me around.

"Unless —" his face clouded momentarily "— unless you've got any plans of your own, that is?"

"No. No, I can't say I've actually got any plans," Kitty said doubtfully. "All the same, could you give me a little time to think it over?"

"Of course, of course," Albert said gruffly. "Though we don't want to leave things until it's too late, do we?"

"Oh, certainly not," Kitty agreed. "I'll give you an answer as soon as I can, but I wouldn't want to rush into anything without thought.

"After all," she went on, picking up her clothes basket, "marriage is such a big step, isn't it?"

Albert's jaw dropped as she went off up the path and disappeared indoors . . .

S HE should have been expecting something like this, Kitty thought as she filled the kettle for her mid-morning cuppa. Ever since she'd moved in, the poor man had fallen over himself trying to be helpful.

And all those flowers and vegetables he had lavished on her. Why, she must have been blind not to realise the implications.

He was obviously a lonely old man, longing for companionship and — and, yes, affection, too. That wasn't a prerogative of the young, after all.

Kitty poured her tea and took it through to the sitting-room. It was all so sudden, that was the trouble. When George had died 15 years ago, it had never entered her head that she might marry again, or even that she might get the opportunity. Now that it had presented itself, what on earth was she going to do?

Kitty avoided her suitor for the next few days, but by the end of the week she was still no nearer a decision.

She liked Albert. In time she might come to like him very much indeed. But when all was said and done, what did she actually *know* about the man?

On the other hand, though, he was obviously a decent, respectable sort. He was a member of the same church she herself had joined on moving to the district, and he had never missed a Sunday in the time she had been going.

And he was such a kindly, considerate soul, too. She would hate to hurt his feelings by refusing him.

Kitty sighed. If only there was someone to advise her, someone she could talk things over with. But she had got to know so few people since moving.

There was no-one really, except — except that nice Mr Braithwaite, she thought suddenly. As spiritual adviser of the parish, he was the natural person to turn to, surely? And he'd been at St Gregory's for nigh on 20 years. If anyone knew Albert, he would.

Putting on her hat and coat, Kitty left her house and set off for the vicarage.

EVERYTHING IN THE GARDEN

FROM behind his net curtains, Albert watched fearfully as she walked down the path. Was she coming in to see him? Had she made her decision?

But, no. She was going past his gate and heading up towards King Street.

Albert felt a wave of temporary relief and returned to his armchair, groaning in unison with the ageing springs.

Of course, he should have told her right away that it was all a misunderstanding. He knew that.

Three times now he had been on the point of going next door to do that very thing, and three times he had taken cold feet.

It was all very well delivering his carefully-worded explanation to the mirror over the sideboard. But delivering it in person to that poor, trusting lady was quite another matter.

Still, it would have to be done. And soon. It would only make things harder for Kitty if he delayed until she had actually accepted his proposal. If she did accept it. There was always the faint hope that she would refuse.

After all, he thought as he set about making some lunch, what did she know about him? From all she was aware, he could be some dreadful old reprobate, instead of the fine, upstanding citizen he undoubtedly was.

The idea began to grow in Albert's mind. He ate his boiled egg, then settled himself by the window to watch for Kitty's return . . .

"Hello, Mrs Black!" He paused by her gate as Kitty fumbled for the key. "Sorry I can't stop. I've got to go down to the bookie, get my line on."

"I didn't know you were a gambling man," she called, her eyebrows raised in surprise.

Albert chuckled. "Oh, I've been following the gee-gees for a long time now. One of my hobbies," he said blithely. "You don't — you don't object to gambling, do you, Kitty?"

"Object? Of course not." She smiled at him. "In fact, hang on a minute and I'll get you down the road. There's one I rather fancy running in the three-thirty."

Albert's new-found optimism faded slightly as they set off for the local bookmaker's.

"No, there's nothing wrong in having a bit of a flutter," she went on gaily, taking his arm.

"That's what I always say." Albert nodded. "It's just that — well, I know there are some self-righteous old spoilsports who would think it foolish to gamble all your pension away. But if you get enjoyment out of it, where's the harm?"

"No harm at all," Kitty said. "We all need a little spice in our lives, don't we?"

Albert grunted, then lapsed into a gloomy silence as they entered the betting shop.

If anything, his silence was even gloomier when they came out again.

"Wasn't I lucky, winning all that money on Bashful Beau!" Kitty said jubilantly. "I'm sorry your horse was last, but I suppose you must be used to losing by this time.

"It was only two pounds, after all," she added consolingly.

Only two pounds, Albert fumed. *Only* two pounds! Why, for little more than half of that, he could have bought a nice little Potentilla from the Garden Centre.

HE was still brooding over his loss the next day, when Kitty came round to invite him for supper.

"That's very kind of you, but you see, I always like to go to the pub on a Saturday night," he explained apologetically.

"During the week I can make do with a few beers at home, but Saturday night just wouldn't be Saturday if I didn't get down to the King's Head for a couple."

Kitty was silent for a moment, and Albert gazed anxiously at her.

"Is anything wrong? I hope you don't disapprove of drink, Kitty?"

"Oh, good gracious, no," she assured him. "I was just thinking it's a long time since I've had a night out myself. Why don't you come over early, then after we've eaten we can go down to the pub together?"

She beamed at him. "There now! Isn't that a good idea?"

"Marvellous!" Albert agreed weakly.

Later that night, crushed up at a corner table in the King's Head, he regarded her blearily over his fifth pint of the landlord's best bitter.

"I've always admired a man who can hold his liquor —" she was chirping. "Cosy little place this, isn't it? I love all those brass plaques, and the pictures of —"

As her voice droned on, Albert fumbled for his newly-acquired pipe. With some difficulty he eventually succeeded in lighting it.

"Hope — hope you don' — don' mind a pipe, Kiddy," he said, coughing as a black, foul-smelling cloud began to grow over their table.

"Not at all, Albert," she assured him. "George, my late husband, used to smoke a pipe, and I always found it rather —"

She broke off, her two eyes merging into one glassy orb that peered at him in concern. "Albert? Albert, are you all right? You've gone a funny green colour. Albert — where are you going?"

A JOKE was a joke, Kitty thought, when she returned from church next day, but this one had gone quite far enough. Poor old Albert! He must really be feeling ill to miss morning service.

She wondered if she should call in and see him, then decided against it. He would probably be having a lie-in. And needing it, too, after his excesses of the previous night.

Still, it served him jolly well right! All that sucking up to her, bringing her flowers and veg! And then that silly roundabout speech on Tuesday! No wonder she'd thought it was marriage he had in mind, and not a take-over bid for her garden.

And she might still be thinking that, too, if it hadn't been for Mr Braithwaite.

Kitty sniffed, her annoyance growing again. "What a nerve!"

It was a good thing she hadn't told the vicar that Albert had offered her marriage. Bad enough him thinking she believed the devious old goat had designs on her.

She blushed again as she remembered Mr Braithwaite's smile on hearing of Albert's courtship.

"Oh, I don't think you need worry about his intentions, Mrs Black," he'd said, laughing. "Albert is a confirmed bachelor if ever I saw one.

"No, I imagine it's your garden he's interested in, rather than your person. He was saying just the other week that he hoped you'd be able to come to some arrangement about it."

Remembering her embarrassment, Kitty's feeling of guilt diminished.

Well, he *had* deserved to be made a fool of, hadn't he, she thought. If he had been straightforward enough to ask for her garden in the first place, all this would never have happened.

But later, when she saw him come up her path, she decided to own up before he pulled any more stunts. Pretending to be a pipe-smoking, gambling alcoholic was bad enough, but she dreaded to think what deterrent he would think up next.

"Hello, Albert. Feeling better, are we?" she asked brightly, as he came in and settled himself in front of the fire.

"No," he said mournfully. "No, I'm not. And it isn't just the drink, so don't be thinking that.

"You see —" He paused, and began fiddling nervously with his tie.

"It's like this —" he tried again, then turned his attention to his cufflinks.

After a moment he abandoned those, too, and looked up at her.

"Kitty, I don't want to get married," he said bluntly.

"I should think not, at your age!" Kitty retorted.

"It's nothing personal, you understand," he went on regardless. "You're a very nice woman, and I'm truly sorry to have disappointed you, but —"

He stopped and glared suspiciously at her. "What d'you mean, you should think not, at my age?"

"Well, it would be ridiculous, wouldn't it? And anyway," she went on, "if you had a wife to consider you wouldn't have so much time for gardening, would you?

"And that would never do. Especially as you've got your eyes on my garden as well as your own!" she finished.

Albert glowered at her, his suspicion turning to outrage.

"Kitty Black, you *knew!* You knew all along, and you let me go on worrying about it, trying to think up ways to put you off!"

"Well, you started it," Kitty said huffily. "And I didn't know all along. You had me just as worried as you were, until that nice Mr Braithwaite told me what you were up to."

"I suppose that makes us even, then, doesn't it?" Albert moved towards the door, then stopped and held out a hand. "No hard feelings?"

Kitty shook it. "None at all, Albert. But aren't you forgetting something?" she added as he made to leave.

Albert turned and raised an eyebrow.

"The garden," Kitty said patiently. "You still haven't asked me about it, you know."

That was one thing he would say for the woman, Albert thought later. She certainly didn't bear a grudge.

And neither could he, not after she'd been decent enough to give him her garden.

He would have to start planning how to use it. It was time to be digging and planting again. Thank heaven the long winter was almost over.

He had always hated winter. At any other time of year, he could busy himself with mowing and planting and digging. There was never any time to feel lonely. But with nothing to do outside, life sometimes seemed as bare and empty as the ground was.

Of course, most people felt a bit isolated in winter, he supposed. At any rate, people who lived alone.

Maybe Kitty did, too, not having had time to make many friends in the neighbourhood.

Albert looked thoughtfully at the wall which divided their two kitchens, then turned his eyes back to the garden.

A small clump of primroses, the first of the season, had bloomed triumphantly.

Picking up his secateurs, he went out and snipped them off. Silly to leave them here when they could bring a bit of cheer inside.

Clutching the flowers, Albert straightened his tie and went next door. □

Complete Story by MARION NAYLOR

"Give Me Your Answer Do!"

But Daisy's bicycle wasn't made just for two. The whole office had jumped aboard!

THERE'S something faintly comic about a bicycle, don't you think?

You might visualise the man of your dreams at the wheel of a sleek Jaguar or even roaring off on a powerful motor-bike — but never pedalling along breathlessly on a bicycle.

Ian Reynolds was hardly the man of anyone's dreams. He'd zip past me in the morning on the way to work, shoulders down, ginger hair rammed under a tight-fitting cap, giving a blurred impression of a flattened question-mark between two circles.

But when Tim Evans joined the firm, I started travelling on an earlier train. It meant I could

meet Tim "accidentally" on the way in, and have his dark-brown eyes and husky voice all to myself for a little while.

Over Tim's elegantly-tailored shoulder I would see Ian Reynolds bounding up the stairs two at a time in his tracksuit top and shorts, humming, "Daisy, Daisy, give me your answer do," just to annoy me.

"Do you all good to join me — you don't know what you're missing!" he'd say sometimes.

He really meant it, too, but his words fell on stony ground — until about a month ago.

The week started badly with a train cancellation. The bus I had to queue four deep for was held up in a traffic jam for twenty minutes. Mr Butler, my boss, was well embarked on his favourite topic when I got to the office.

"Time is money," he said, stopping in his caged-lion prowl to glare at me, "and so is heat. I can't afford to heat empty offices. Do you realise what our overheads are?"

"Yes, Mr Butler," Miss Jenkins said apologetically, though I really don't know what she had to be apologetic about, since she always caught a bus at dawn just in case the Boss might get to the office before her.

Miss Jenkins was part of the fittings. Sometimes she dressed in grey to match the filing cabinet, and sometimes in fawn to tone with the panelling — a pity, because she had a heart of gold and deserved a better fate.

"GIVE ME YOUR ANSWER DO!"

O N Tuesday, the train was half an hour late because of ailing points, and Miss Jenkins said, "Oh dear, Daisy, Mr Butler isn't very pleased."

On Wednesday, the train before mine had broken down, so mine had a double load. We'd gone two stations before I could put the other foot down. What with the cigarette smoke and a man built like a wrestler standing on my foot, there were still tears in my eyes when I reached work.

Mr Crump was extricating himself from his old car. Waving cheerfully, he kicked the door shut, whereupon a headlamp dropped off. He pushed it back into place and straightened his bulk, breathing hard.

Being a bachelor, he had no-one to balance his diet, and he stoked himself up from the confectioner's round the corner.

Just then Ian Reynolds swept between us and dismounted with a single lithe movement.

"Lovely morning!" he said, beaming at us both.

Later in the morning he came down to our office, looking almost normal in the jacket and trousers he changed into at work, said, "Hi!" to me and handed a file over to Miss Jenkins.

She took it over to the shelves behind Mr Crump, then she hesitated.

"Allow me," Mr Crump said automatically, his eyes still on his desk — very few people ever really looked at poor Miss Jenkins. He climbed on his chair to reach the top shelf.

NOSTALGIA

O, to reverse life's moving
    times
for the happy days of
    youth,
To find again the friends
    I loved,
and see the way we were.
The things we did, the
    games we played,
and joys we learned to
    share,
We laughed and cried as
    time rolled by
but never seemed to care.
Picnics on a river bank,
    swimming in a pool,
excitement felt when time

came round
for holidays from school.
I wonder where they all
    are now,
those dear old pals so
    true,
And if they sometimes
    think of me,
Or of the times we knew.
To return again, to those
    happy days
of times so swiftly flown.
For just one fleeting
    moment,
I would give everything
    I own.
                — Mr J. H. M., nr Chester.

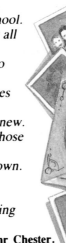

"By jove," he grunted, "I'll have to get fit — think I could lose a bit of weight."

"A bike, that's what you want," Ian said, with his usual crusading zeal. "Regular exercise, fresh air. No rushing for trains. No *crowds,*" he added, looking in my direction. "You can't beat cycling."

"Cycling?" The Boss had appeared at his door. "Blasted nuisance, cyclists. No road sense. No consideration. A menace on the road.

"Ought to pay road tax, and reduce mine a bit," he added, prowling. "Do you all *eat* pencils in this place? Have you any idea how much I spend a year on office equipment?"

THAT night I listened to the weather forecast, which was optimistic, excavated my old bike from the garage and tried it cautiously round the block.

In the morning, I slung my bag in the front basket and wobbled furtively out into the sunshine. After I'd free-wheeled lazily down the hill, instead of running frantically up it to the station, and swept smugly past several bus queues, I was beginning to enjoy myself. Two pedals and a whole saddle to myself . . .

Ian Reynold's ginger eyebrows rose in amazement.

"Well, I never! Good for Daisy! Enjoy it, did you?"

Without waiting for an answer, he started to prod the tyres and spin the pedals experimentally.

"Could do with a bit of an overhaul," he said.

I left him wrenching the handlebars back to the right position, and went to comb my hair before Tim arrived, ready to start work.

"It seems," Tim said, with tolerant amusement, "to be catching." His lop-sided smile made my heart do a big-dipper lurch.

The day after, Mr Crump went down with it as well. He trundled in after me, all fourteen stones of him, miraculously supported by half an inch of air front and back.

"I can feel it doing me good already," he panted.

We swapped cyclists' tales of near misses and maniac car drivers until Mr Butler arrived. He was furious because they'd just put up the parking fees to a scandalous seventy-five pence a day.

"Have you both cycled?" Miss Jenkins asked, wide-eyed.

That was enough to trigger off me and Mr Crump.

"You can set off when you like —"

"And the exercise — you're bound to lose pounds —"

"And it's so cheap —"

The Boss appeared. "What's cheap?" he asked.

"Cycling, Mr Butler."

"I suppose it must be," he said, with an air of discovery.

"Gives you an appetite," Mr Crump said, through a mouthful of currant bun.

"And it's so clean — it doesn't add to pollution." I got quite carried away. "No exhaust fumes — no risk to the community."

"GIVE ME YOUR ANSWER DO!"

Miss Jenkins was distressed. "Oh, dear, I suppose I am partly responsible — it never occurred to me before that I was encouraging pollution — I feel quite guilty."

Miss Jenkins came to work by bus, you see.

Three days later she pedalled decorously through the gate on a low, small-wheeled machine, a prudently long skirt billowing round her calves.

"My, you've got some gumption!" Mr Crump looked at her as if for the first time and her pale cheeks flushed becomingly.

The Boss was immune to anti-pollution arguments or the lure of keeping fit. But any possibility of saving money always lowered his resistance.

He lived miles from the railway, so in a bid to cheat the car park sharks, he tried the bus. When he finally got in, there was a pulse beating ominously in his temple and he was muttering, "Time — all that time — wasted. And time's money . . ."

His bike was a sturdy, second-hand roadster with a carrier on the back for his black briefcase.

THERE followed a golden fortnight.

"The Butler Brothers Cycling Club," Tim, our only non-cyclist, murmured as we all swooped in one morning.

We didn't go mad, like Ian Reynolds. I simply exchanged high heels for flatties, and Miss Jenkins her felt hat for a pink headscarf, which let a casual curl escape and matched the new glow in her cheeks.

"Pink suits you," I heard Mr Crump say. He looked quite dashing himself in his checked sports jacket.

Mr Butler's sole concession was a pair of cycling clips, but he was as happy as anyone. It was all free, and we were getting to work on time. Since he'd be miserable without something to grumble at, he'd found a new target.

"Ruddy motorists!" he'd say. "One of them pulled across my handlebars this morning — nearly had me off. I gave it to him properly. He won't do it again in a hurry," he added with satisfaction. "Think they own the road just because they pay road tax."

Really, it was idyllic.

And then the storm came. There were only a few drops of rain as I wheeled my bike out of our gate, but I'd put on my new light-weight shower-proof and a beret just in case.

Before I'd gone two miles it was coming down steadily. I was trying, with one hand, to pull my coat over the darkening triangle of skirt and feeling cold raindrops trickling down the back of my neck.

It was then that I had to dismount to see what the sudden jolting was.

I'd never mended a puncture before. Anyway, I'd nothing to mend it with. I didn't even have a pump. One minute I was sweeping arrogantly past pavement plodders, and the next I was stuck. I gazed at the bike helplessly.

And then I saw Tim hurrying towards me with his black umbrella — sane, stolid, capable. The *relief.*

"Thank goodness!" I said. "I've got a puncture and I'm soaked. What shall I do?"

Tim felt the back tyre gingerly with his clean, well-manicured hand.

"Leave it here," he said at last. "Behind the wall — perhaps one of the vans might pick it up."

"What — just abandon it?" I felt a sudden affection for it.

"Having trouble?" a voice said, and there was Ian Reynolds, my knight-errant, in a yellow cape and peaked cap.

In no time at all I was in a shop doorway with my wet coat off and a yellow cape on. The bike was upside down, its tyre already half off.

WHEN at last we reached the office, only Mr Crump was there, trying to soothe an important-looking visitor who was looking angrily at his watch.

"My appointment," he said, "was for nine-fifteen, and I am a very busy man."

There wasn't much we could do. Where on earth was Miss Jenkins, let alone the Boss?

We watched the visitor striding out through the gate. Just as Miss Jenkins wheeled a badly-buckled machine in through it.

She came in moaning, "Oh, dear! Oh, dear!" like the White Rabbit, and trying to wipe her glasses with a shaking hand.

Mr Crump helped her tenderly out of the muddy pink coat she'd bought three days ago. She told us about her skid, pausing frequently to ask, "But where *is* Mr Butler? Such an important appointment . . ."

I saw him first, actually, from the window. He wheeled his bike in, flung it into a corner, then threw the broken chain on top of it. He stamped across to the door with black hands and looks to match. Prudently, I found business along the corridor, so I heard only the tail end of the tirade.

"Don't talk to me about cycling. Cheap? *Cheap?* With one customer lost and a suit covered in grease? Do you know how much cleaning costs?"

The cycling epidemic was over three weeks after it had begun.

Miss Jenkins has forgotten the evils of pollution and willingly accepts a lift every day in Mr Crump's car — though, interestingly, it means he has to drive right out of his way. He found, unfortunately, that all that pedalling had made him eat more . . .

Mr Butler is back in his car, too. The experiment has not been completely in vain, because the other day I distinctly saw him slow down and wave on a cyclist from a side road.

And me? Well, yes, I've abandoned my bike as well. Ian and I find a tandem so much more convenient. □

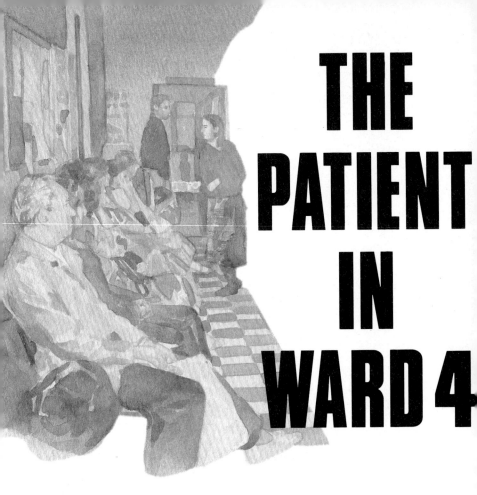

THE PATIENT IN WARD 4

I PRACTISED with the crutches in the privacy of my own room and was annoyed to discover how awkward and unnatural the whole business of learning to walk with them could be.

I was not a patient pupil but the nurses were undaunted by my frustration, and eventually I became proficient enough to exercise along the corridor.

It was there I met Elaine.

She was a patient, too, but her case was obviously much less serious than mine. My leg had been badly broken and was in plaster to the knee, while her cast merely encased her right foot.

On our first encounter we just exchanged nods of mutual sympathy as we passed each other, but I felt that the obvious difference in our injuries must have made her realise that she wasn't so badly off.

The next day we met again. It was at this stage I realised that she

In only a few days she
taught him a lesson
that he had failed to
learn in a lifetime . . .

Complete
Story
by
CHARLES C.
O'CONNELL

THE PATIENT IN WARD 4

was a very striking girl; tall, only a little shorter than my five feet eleven, with dark hair swept back from her forehead and usually caught at the nape of a long, slender neck.

The day before, like myself, she had worn a dressing-gown over pyjamas, but now, although she still wore the gown, she had a polo-neck sweater under it. I had the distinct impression that I had seen her somewhere before.

As I was passing her, one of my crutches skidded fractionally on the polished floor, and she stopped in alarm as I struggled to regain my composure.

"Are you all right?" she asked anxiously.

"These things are a nuisance," I said, feeling a fool, "but they're better than the wheel-chairs."

"You don't like using a wheelchair?"

"No, I don't. It makes me feel old."

It also made me feel inferior, but I didn't say that. Everything I had done in life had been done on my feet, looking other men straight in the eyes, proving myself as good or better than they were . . .

As she smiled faintly, I said, "Do you mind if I walk along with you?"

Although she said nothing about her injury, I knew she was worried about it. It showed in her eyes — dark eyes that seemed to change colour with her moods.

I didn't mean to confide in her at all, and I don't know why I did. I haven't told many people that I made it the hard way. For instance, I had no formal education and knew real poverty in my youth — which taught you to fight for survival . . .

Of course, I didn't burden Elaine with all of that. I told her mostly of the successful part of my life; how I had struggled to build up a large haulage business from a single box-cart which I once trundled through the streets as a boy.

I was doing well now, which was the reason I could afford to have a private room in this orthopaedic hospital, with the best doctors and surgeons in attendance on me.

That's about all I told her that day, and I had misgivings about it later on. I felt that I had talked too much about myself, while she had said very little. From even that little I couldn't recall anything except her name. But that was typical of me then: what anybody else said meant little to me. But this was the first time it had ever worried me.

I wondered a lot about her that night — where she came from, what she did, where she lived — but I realised that I couldn't just ask her outright about these things without appearing nosey.

WE met again the next morning and every morning after that, always at the same time as though by agreement. Although some days we didn't have the corridor to ourselves, as far as I was concerned she was the only person I could see.

I did most of the talking, digging up every funny incident from my background to keep her amused. All this because I had noticed that, in repose, her features assumed a sad look, as though she were brooding on her injury.

She must have found many of my anecdotes amusing because she laughed frequently. That was a real tonic to me, and, I hoped, to her.

At the end of the week my transport manager and my accountant visited me and brought reams of work. This annoyed me a little in spite of the fact that I had instructed them to bring in the accounts.

It was past noon when I finally got rid of them, and by then I had missed Elaine. I hobbled up and down the corridor for a while but she didn't appear.

My surgeon turned up that evening and told me I could leave the following day, although I would have to endure the plaster cast for some weeks to come.

I had wanted to discharge myself a week before but he had advised against it. Now he wanted to get rid of me just when I'd found somebody interesting to talk to!

I told him it was inconvenient for me to go the following day. He felt that after eight weeks yet another day wouldn't make any difference.

Next morning in the corridor I saw a lot of people come out of ward four — Elaine's ward. There were not many private rooms and judging by the number of visitors who emerged, I guessed that Elaine shared the ward with other patients.

They didn't look very special, five men and four women, all appearing pretty grim as if their visit had depressed them. They passed by without looking at me. I didn't blame them for that. Before I broke my leg I'd have passed the most pitiful plastered wreck without a glance . . .

When they had disappeared, Elaine turned up. Straightaway I knew she had been crying.

I fell in beside her without being invited, feeling that all attempts to make her happy had been undone . . .

After a while I said, "Visitors can be darned depressing."

She actually laughed, although there was a small catch in her laughter.

"Do you have many visitors?" she asked me.

"Not really," I told her. "Just people from the business. I have no living relatives. I'm afraid I don't remember my father, and my mother died some years ago."

"I'm sorry," she said.

"So am I. She died at a time when I could have given her everything she wanted. I moved her into a fine house with people to look after her, but she died within a year. She was just worn out."

"That was a pity," Elaine said.

"That's life," I said. "Life is tough, as you probably know."

Elaine looked at me thoughtfully for a moment, and I was pleased to see that the tears were gone.

"I enjoyed life," she said. "Well, I enjoyed it up till now."

The last part had me worried. I said, "Well, keep on enjoying it. You mustn't worry about your foot, especially when you're young and beautiful."

When she looked at me again I thought her eyes were twinkling and I was sure I had bucked her up enormously. But I still sensed an underlying and persistent anxiety about her. Something was bothering this girl and it had me worried, too.

Next morning I put on my blue suit with a pale blue shirt and tie to match, and went into the corridor. My bag was packed and Derek, my driver, was coming around in the car for me within the hour.

I think Elaine was disappointed when she saw me ready for departure.

"I'm being discharged today," I told her.

She didn't look very happy about that. "I'm sorry you're leaving," she said. And then she seemed confused. "I mean, I'm glad you're fit enough to be discharged, but I will miss your company."

Nobody had ever said anything like that to me in my life and it made me feel good.

"You've made the last week very enjoyable," I said. "I'd like to

see you again, if you wouldn't mind. I could come to visit you here."
Her eyes were laughing now, and I felt a bit awkward.
"I'd like that, very much," she said.
"In the meantime," I told her, "you mustn't worry about anything.
Just give yourself a chance to get well and I'll come around to see
you. I promise I won't depress you."
"I can never imagine you doing that." She laughed.
Derek came along then, early and over-anxious, as usual. He
carried a rug over his arm as if he expected to drape it around me. I
said goodbye to Elaine then, giving her my telephone number just in
case there might be something I could do for her.
Derek drove me home to the big house I had built beside the
depot. There his wife, who cooked and kept house for the three of
us, nearly drove me mad with her concern for me.
I liked Derek's wife, but prolonged exposure to fussy concern
weakens a man. Besides, I felt depressed, mainly because there
wouldn't be any more morning walks with Elaine and also because,
away from the snug security of hospital, some of the confidence I had
in my leg had deserted me.

FOUR days later I came downstairs unassisted to breakfast.
Derek deplored my intention of going to work so soon, and
his wife came out of the kitchen with my breakfast, looking
as if she expected me to collapse at the table. She put the folded
newspaper beside my plate.
Then Derek said, "There's a picture in the paper of that young
lady you were talking to in the hospital."
I had always suspected he read the paper before I saw it, but right
then I didn't mind any more.
"It's on page twelve," he said.
Sure enough, there she was. She looked lovely. There was also a
story about her.
Apparently it had just been announced that there was little doubt
now that this famous ballerina would dance again after making a
complete recovery from injuries sustained during rehearsal some
months before, when a heavy prop had fallen on her right foot.
The announcement ended a grim period of agonised speculation as
to whether the world-renowned ballerina would ever dance again.
The article went on to chronicle her successes in London, Paris,
Berlin, Moscow, New York . . .
There had I been boring her with details of my great injuries, and
all the while she had listened to me patiently and sympathetically, not
knowing if her own life was in ruins.
I didn't eat breakfast, and this precipitated some panic, but I
handled Derek and his wife quietly and politely. It occurred to me
then that they, too, could have problems I knew nothing about.
My unusual behaviour seemed to give them the impression that I

was seriously ill, but I had never felt better or more certain of what I was going to do in my life.

DURING my first day at work I discovered several mistakes made during my absence, but between myself, the transport manager and the accountant, we ironed everything out. They were very apologetic, and dumbfounded when I waived their apologies.

For the first time in my life I'd been forced to take a long, hard look at myself.

After my encounter with Elaine I was still feeling ashamed of my self-centred attitude. Other people did have problems. It was such an obvious fact of life. Yet I'd always been so busy pushing and clawing my way to the top that I'd never before given it any thought.

So for the next two days, I hobbled around the depot, getting to know the people who worked for me, listening to their grievances and promising to think about them.

The result was a much improved incentive scheme for the drivers and maintenance men, and a much better understanding between me and my employees.

There was no question now of going to see Elaine. If she remembered me at all it would be as the patient whose brash boastfulness had sometimes amused her.

One morning about two weeks later, my secretary wanted to know if I would see somebody who hadn't an appointment. I agreed. But I was astounded when she showed Elaine into the office, sat her down and propped her crutches against the wall before going out.

I felt myself blushing guiltily as Elaine said, "You didn't come back to visit me."

It was only then that I believed she was actually in my office and was not an illusion created by my yearning for her.

"I read about you in the paper," I said. "I was too ashamed to visit you — after all my talk back there in hospital, me shooting my mouth off, while all the while you . . . "

"I missed you," she cut in. "Life became very dull after you left." Her level, wistful gaze was very disturbing. She looked even more beautiful than I remembered.

"I'm glad you will be able to dance again," I stammered. "I didn't know who you were in the hospital."

"I'm glad you didn't," she said quietly. "You cheered me up tremendously. I'd be sorry to think that I'd be deprived of your strength and encouragement in the future just because you now know what I do."

I fervently wished I could move around to her then, but my plaster cast seemed to be nailed to the floor. We just sat and looked at each other, my mind already charged with the things of the future, and none of them anything to do with business. □

Then Along Came Christabel

Complete Story by D. L. GARRARD

She came into their lives like a whirlwind, bringing chaos, laughter and romance.

JANET BASSET stood in her kitchen, reading her aunt's letter over again.

It would make me feel much easier, Janet, if Christabel could stay with you while she's in London on this training course. You know Christabel — everything happens to her, and if it doesn't, she makes it! She's changed her job half a dozen times since she left school. How am I to know she won't suddenly change her mind yet again, and find herself with neither job nor money? It wouldn't occur to her to write home for help. She'd just go on making things worse. Anything could happen in two weeks!

Janet smiled and shook her head. Aunt Sybil never stopped worrying. Janet hadn't seen Christabel, her cousin, for several years. She must be eighteen by now — surely old enough to take care of herself?

THEN ALONG CAME CHRISTABEL

Janet could remember that, at ten years old, Christy would listen to the advice of her older cousin, but she wouldn't be likely to take much notice now.

Still, it would be pleasant to see her cousin again — thin, freckle-faced Christy, with her turned-up nose and golden red hair, never out of trouble but still delightful company.

The splutter of bacon under the grill brought Janet back to Monday morning and the fact that she'd miss her usual bus if she didn't hurry. Quickly she made coffee and ate her breakfast. She believed in a proper start to the day. She was as organised as Christabel was scatter-brained.

THE girls at the office were always joking about Janet's way of life. They borrowed all sorts of things from her, from safety-pins to her handbag sewing-kit for instant repairs. They would sigh over their own shortcomings and admire Janet's ordered existence. But there were times when Janet suspected they thought her a bit too cautious and serious.

"It's no use, though, I just couldn't be any other way," she'd explain to Gerry Thurston. "You know me — I've always been the same."

Gerry would know if any one did. He and Janet had lived in the same street, gone to the same schools, and by coincidence got jobs with the same company. When Janet's father's firm moved out of the city and her parents followed, she moved into her small flat and she and Gerry still met regularly on Tuesdays and Saturdays.

Tomorrow evening, she'd have a word with Gerry and see if he could find someone to make up a foursome for one or two of Christy's evenings. She'd no doubt be a bit lost at first, after a lifetime of the countryside, falling out of trees and into rivers — and falling foul of almost everyone with authority!

Janet went off to work, still making plans.

During the morning someone came round collecting for a wedding present.

"For Judy West? But she only met David at Christmas, didn't she?" Janet queried, dropping her contribution into the envelope.

"Yes, but why hesitate when you've found the right person? We're all waiting for you and Gerry to set a date!"

Janet laughed, blushing slightly. Her relationship with Gerry was safe, pleasant. It wasn't *the* romance she hoped would come along one day.

Janet wasn't given to romantic dreams, but she did hope that life promised more than a grown-up version of the boy who'd once won every marble she possessed, and whose scarred knees she knew as well as her own!

Perhaps because she felt restless, she decided not to wait until the following day to see Gerry. She knew he played squash at the company's sports club on Mondays. When she arrived, it was to find that he was on court, so she waited patiently.

Eventually he appeared, laughing at some joke he was sharing with the girl walking with him.

Janet noticed how attractive she looked in her whites. Gerry wore shorts and a T-shirt and seemed more animated than usual.

"Why, Janet!"

For a second he looked startled, then he smiled broadly at her.

"This is Pam from the accounts department. You may have seen her in the office. It's a surprise to see you here. Fancy joining the squash club?"

"I'm not sure I've that kind of energy," Janet said lightly. "I'd settle for a nice swim but I'll leave squash to the more energetic! No, that's not what brought me here.

"I had some interesting news today, that's all. I looked in, hoping for the chance to tell you over a coffee."

"There's a few of us arranged to go for a bite to eat. Why don't you join us? We can chat on the way." Gerry took her arm as he spoke.

"It's not all that important," Janet found herself saying. She didn't know any of the others, and for some reason felt out of it. When she saw Pam still waiting around for Gerry, Janet felt oddly uncomfortable.

"It can wait — it was just a thought. I happened to be passing," she added. "I'll see you tomorrow. I should be getting on with some ironing anyway."

Normally she quite enjoyed ironing, seeing everything emerging smooth and fresh, but that evening it seemed a rather dull thing to be doing.

Next morning, she wasted no time telling Gerry the news about Christabel. He agreed it would be pleasant to make a foursome, and he'd try to find someone suitable for Christabel.

"I hardly know the girl, Janet," he said. "Your Aunt Sybil always invited you and the family to go and stay with her. She hated London, didn't she?"

But Janet was too busy to bring Gerry up to date about Christabel. She was too preoccupied making the preparations for her guest.

Christabel phoned Janet the night before she was due to arrive.

"Oh, Jan, I've been too busy to write — sorry! Thanks for finding room for me. I'm really dying to see you again. Fancy you having a flat in town. It doesn't sound a bit like you, all among the bright lights!"

"But I've always lived here," Janet protested, laughing.

"Oh, but with your parents. Now it's different, isn't it? Now you can please yourself, have parties, do mad things, come home in the small hours with nobody to nag you about all that beauty sleep you're losing."

THEN ALONG CAME CHRISTABEL

CHRISTABEL sounded just like the mischievous, impulsive girl of old, except that the voice was no longer childish, but had a trace of huskiness. Janet arranged to meet her at the station straight from the office on Tuesday evening. It meant cancelling her Tuesday date with Gerry, but Christabel was on a two-week course, beginning on Wednesday.

"Shall I wear a red rose?" Christy joked. "So you'll recognise me?"

"Wouldn't it clash with your hair?" Janet teased back, remembering the plaits and freckles.

"You sound like Mum. She throws a fit if I wear blue and green together. Tell you what — I'll wear my red suit, then you can't possibly miss me!"

Sure enough, Christabel burst through between the other passengers like a blazing arrow. Yellow frills from her blouse frothed over her collar and she carried a shoulder bag and hold-all in shades of red which argued with her suit, as did the suitcase she carried in her other hand.

"Janet — dear old Jan!" Janet was enveloped in a cloud of perfume and a wild jangling of bracelets and chains as Christy bent to embrace her. Yes, bent!

The incredibly high heels were partly to blame, but Christy had grown from a wiry shrimp into a magnificent five foot six.

"I'd have known you anywhere, Jan, except for your hair." Christy put Janet at arm's length to study her critically. "It would suit you better shorter now, you know, but that's the hairdresser in me speaking from three jobs ago!

"How are you? We were naughty not to write — such a lot to catch up on. I must tell you my own version of my life story as opposed to my mother's, which must have filled you with doubts about having me under your roof!"

"Not at all," Janet said breathlessly when she could get a word in. "Let me take your case. Is this all the luggage you brought?"

"Oh, heavens, no. I forgot in all the excitement." Christy spun around. "Oh, there you are. Janet, this is Jim. I collected him on the train and he's kindly saved me the trouble of a porter. Jim . . . what was it? Hedley?"

"Hendley," Jim corrected patiently. He was fair, blue-eyed and burdened with two enormous suitcases which matched the one Christy carried.

He smiled at Janet. "Hello there. If I can persuade Christabel to stay on the subject long enough to arrange something, I rather hope we might be meeting again. Would I be right in assuming you're her chaperone?"

Janet looked at Christabel. Perhaps her cousin had been pestered by this young man and would rather be rid of him? But Christabel laughed and spread her arms, nearly knocking over a passer-by.

"Sorry, folk! I always talk non-stop when I'm excited. All right. Tonight? Tomorrow?"

"Christy, give yourself time to settle in!" Janet exclaimed, then blushed as she realised how much she sounded just like the chaperone Jim Hendley had taken her for.

"I'm afraid I'm tied up until the weekend," Jim said. "Could we make up a foursome on Saturday evening, perhaps?" He turned to Janet. "I know a very nice nightclub with a cabaret and dancing."

He had a nice smile, Janet thought, somewhat disarmed. "I could bring a friend on Saturday," she agreed.

Now she and Gerry wouldn't have to miss their next meeting. Nor would he have to worry about finding a friend to make up numbers. She remembered, in a bit of a daze, the old feeling of being caught up in Christy's whirlwind.

"Good," Jim was saying. "I'll pick you all up by taxi — eight o'clock?"

He took Janet's address and phone number, before seeing them on their way.

Christy explored the flat with pleasure.

"I'm sorry there's not a proper room to yourself," Janet apologised. "It's a sort of annexe off my bedroom, but it holds a folding bed nicely, and there's a little chest of drawers. I put up a curtain in the doorway for privacy. I hope you'll be comfortable."

"It's fine. I hope I'm not being too much trouble, that's all. Mother just wouldn't be convinced I'd manage on my own, but I wanted to see you again anyway."

Janet smiled wryly as she went to put the kettle on, and check the casserole she'd left cooking in her slow cookpot.

"It seems to me I was always preventing you from doing things you wanted to!" Janet laughed. "You must have looked on me as a killjoy, being older and usually put in charge."

"Like now, for instance," Christy added teasingly. She kicked off her shoes, threw her jacket on the bed and came back over to Janet.

"Sometimes I wished you'd forget yourself," she admitted. "But I really looked up to you, you know. Anyway, it doesn't matter a hoot now. Usually I'd managed to do what I wanted before you came out with the big-sister act!"

THEN ALONG CAME CHRISTABEL

She prowled round the flat. "This is a super place, really. You could do things with it."

"I've done what I want, mostly," Janet replied.

"Don't you read any of the glossy magazines? There are all kinds of things advertised for making a place look trendy. I'm dying to have a mooch round some of the big stores," she went on. "Oh, Janet, isn't life exciting? You never know what's round the next corner."

Janet stopped herself from saying she preferred to have some inkling of what lay ahead. Christabel's effervescence amused her. She began to serve the meal.

"Well, this corner of the road shouldn't hold any horrible surprises. This is one of my favourite recipes, and it usually turns out well."

"All your things do. You seem to be good at everything," Christy said, sniffing appreciatively.

She was sounding like the girls at the office, Janet thought.

"My life might appear a bit sedate to you."

"I'll soon change that!" Christy laughed mischievously. "Now bring me up to date, Janet. Mum said you were still seeing Gerry — after all these years! I believe I met him once when I came to stay, but I scarcely remember him."

"He's a good friend, that's all," Janet said lightly. "We meet Tuesdays. Sometimes we just walk around old London, or in the summer take the Tube out of town. Saturdays, it's usually the cinema, or a meal at some small restaurant. Nothing exciting really, but they're things we enjoy together."

Christy sprang to her feet, jolting the table. "That reminds me. I bought a bottle of wine to celebrate our being together again."

She unpacked her hold-all all over the lounge before she found it at the bottom . . .

THE week flew by, leaving Janet quite breathless. Apart from her time at the training centre, Christy wanted to cram the whole of London into a fortnight.

"What are you wearing?" she demanded of Janet when it came to Saturday evening. "I don't know whether to wear my green, or this cream thing."

Clearly she favoured the green shimmery frock with the sequin motif on one shoulder. The other shoulder simply wasn't there!

Janet replied dubiously, "But we aren't going to paint the town or anything, are we? I thought I'd just wear my pale blue. Gerry rather likes it."

"Jan, you can't! I've been asking around at the training centre, and this nightclub is quite swish. Yes — it's the green one for me. It makes me look a bit mermaidy and I don't often get a chance to wear it."

"Well, I don't know . . . Gerry and I don't go in for this kind of thing. I haven't anything much out of the ordinary. Certainly not as glamorous as your dress."

"Well, it's time you did." Christy was busy whisking through Janet's wardrobe. She held up a brown velvet skirt.

"Oh no, you don't!" she cried and snatched the demure white blouse Janet reached for and hung it back on the rail. "I've got something else that'll go with this skirt beautifully."

By eight o'clock, Janet found herself in the long skirt with a beautiful lacy blouse in a coffee colour. She had given up protesting and even allowed her cousin to do her make-up for her, using colours that Janet herself would never have considered.

"From now on, you'll wear make-up every day!" Christabel commanded.

"But I do," Janet protested, knowing Christy was referring to the eye-shadows, blushers and liners which lay all over her own bedroom.

"I do look rather . . . different," Janet admitted, gazing at her reflection.

"But you really should have your hair trimmed. You need a change now and then. Oh, there's the doorbell."

IT was Gerry. Janet felt an unexpected pang of pleasure when she saw his expression — then she realised he was staring at Christy, who did one of her now familiar dives into the bedroom for something she'd forgotten.

"If they only knew what they'd missed!" he murmured humorously to Janet.

"They? Oh — you mean the men you asked who couldn't make up our foursome?"

"Wouldn't, I'm afraid. I had to be honest — I misled them. They asked what she was like and I had only one memory to go on. Christy was falling off your bicycle at the time, as I remember, all teeth and legs. And I said she was your young cousin and . . . there's your doorbell again."

This time it was Jim. Janet followed the other three out of the flat. Gerry's words were ringing in her ears. When he'd said he'd described Christy as her young cousin, among other things, and no-one had thought she'd be interesting, did that mean that she, too, appeared uninteresting?

But Gerry was murmuring in her ear now.

"You look nice tonight, Janet." But somehow it didn't dispel the feeling of doubt. She was still rather distant even when Jim and Gerry dropped them back at the flat.

THEN ALONG CAME CHRISTABEL

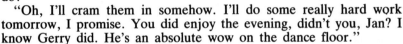

"Super evening," Christy said, kicking off her shoes the moment they were back through the door. "But why aren't you seeing Gerry before we go out again next Saturday?"

"We've other interests, Christy. And at the moment, I also have you," Janet replied lightly.

"But I'll be going out with Jim."

"Christy, I don't want to spoil your fun and lecture you, but haven't you some studies to do?"

"Oh, I'll cram them in somehow. I'll do some really hard work tomorrow, I promise. You did enjoy the evening, didn't you, Jan? I know Gerry did. He's an absolute wow on the dance floor."

Janet herself hadn't realised how well Gerry could dance. He'd remarked that the nightclub was just right for a special evening and he'd make a note of it. For a night out with Pam? she wondered. Or perhaps for someone else he'd gone out with that Janet didn't even know about?

Suddenly she'd seen her own life as an open book, but Gerry's seemed to have whole chapters she'd never read, in spite of all their years as friends.

"I'll see you on Tuesday, will I?" he'd said to her as they parted.

"No, afraid not," she had replied on a wild impulse.

Let there be a few mysterious passages in her own book, instead of every page being so predictable. Perhaps Jim would produce an exciting friend; perhaps she'd have a romantic encounter on the bus, in the lift, or going to the grocer's? In Christy's life a thousand things could happen in one day, so why not in hers?

Nothing new did happen before Friday, of course, except to Christy, who was adopted on the Tube by a stray kitten!

"It was ambling along the edge of the platform in deadly danger," she cried. "Nobody wanted to know about it, so I brought it back. I'll call her Anastasia. I've always wanted a kitten called Anastasia."

Janet accepted the kitten's arrival without too much surprise. During the week, her flat had already acquired an exotic bead curtain in place of the cotton one at the annexe door; a bushy plant potted in the back of an enormous ceramic frog; and one which climbed up a trellis in the kitchen and kept getting in the way.

In the evening, Janet had just washed her hair when Christy arrived back from a disco where she'd been with friends she'd made at the training centre that week.

"You're home early," Janet remarked. "No good?'

"Oh, the disco was all right. But it turned out Ted had ideas other than dancing."

She flopped on to the settee.

"Funny — well, silly really, but I kept feeling I shouldn't even be with Ted. I met Jim only ten days ago, and five and a half hours, to be exact.

"That's going back to the moment on the train when I spilled my coffee all over his new paperback and he looked up and smiled at me. And that was it — I can't help it. I only hope, quite desperately, that Jim feels the same way about me."

INWARDLY Janet was feeling a little desperate herself. The week had been just as usual, except for the gap on Tuesday. With no Gerry, she'd made a determined excursion to the swimming baths, but it only proved how out of condition she was.

"I shouldn't think that's any problem," Janet answered, trying not to sound wistful.

"Oh, I'm just afraid it'll be over as suddenly as it started. I wish some of your confident calm would rub off on me, Jan. Nobody ever thinks of me as being unsure, but believe me, that's what's behind most of my escapades. I'm always afraid I've done the wrong thing, made the wrong choice, and trying to jump away before it's too late.

"Oh well, forget about me! There's nothing wrong with you, Jan, is there? You look as if you've got the glooms, too."

Unable to explain her own mixed-up feelings, Janet murmured, "I was just thinking my hair looks a mess. I was going to have it done for tomorrow night, but . . ."

Christy looked suddenly alert. "You were to buy a new dress, you said. Did you?"

"No. I didn't think it was worth it for one night."

Christy leaped up. "Oh, don't be silly. You're going to treat yourself. We'll start out early tomorrow. As for your hair, you suit it soft and natural. There's no need to spend the earth at a salon.

"All it needs is an inch or so off the ends, and flicked up. I can easily do that. Come on, let me do it now and we can experiment with styles."

"Are you sure?" Janet looked at her doubtfully.

"I learned how to cut, rest assured. I even carry my hairdressing scissors with me to trim my own occasionally. I'll get a towel to put round your shoulders. Sit in front of your mirror, then you can watch."

Janet put her doubts aside, but preferred to watch the kitten's reflection rather than her own, as it capered about on the settee.

"Strange, isn't it," she said, "how we rarely see ourselves as others see us? I always thought you were full of confidence. Why, even at ten years old you . . . oh — look out! Anastasia will tear your new scarf!"

Christabel spun round just as Janet twisted her head. The scissors, about to snip off a careful inch at the back of her head, bit into a large chunk instead. Kitten and scarf forgotten, both girls stared petrified at the jagged lump of hair in Christy's hand. Janet felt the back of her head with something like terror. The remaining tuft felt incredibly short.

She felt near to tears. She'd been at a disadvantage ever since her cousin arrived — and now this! What would Gerry feel, having to take her out looking like a half-shorn lamb!

Then one realisation followed another so rapidly that they took her breath away. It wasn't just that she looked peculiar, but that she wanted Gerry to see her at her best. He mattered, and in a different way to what she'd imagined all these years. The friendship hadn't been static after all, but blossoming underground into something more.

That's why the sight of Pam at the sports club had started the uneasiness she hadn't been able to pin down. It wasn't a wild new romance she wanted, but simply the continuing of her totally satisfying relationship with Gerry, whom she loved and trusted.

"Christy, can't you do anything about my hair?"

"Yes!" Christabel announced firmly. "There's only one thing to do, and I'm going to take a leaf out of your book, Jan, and have the confidence to do it. Just close your eyes and don't say a word, or you'll spoil my concentration."

The scissors clicked busily, frighteningly close to Janet's head. She had no desire to peep, being overwhelmed by her own emotions.

"There. No — don't look yet. Where's the hairdryer? I'll blow-dry it for you."

They stared at her finished reflection in silence. The dry hair, short and feathery, gave her an entirely different appearance. Janet swallowed hard as it dawned on her that Christy had been successful this time.

"It looks . . . rather nice," she said cautiously.

BY late Saturday afternoon, Janet was prepared to go to the ball in none other than Cinderella's apron if only Christabel would ease up. But Christy wouldn't, until she found exactly the dress she had in mind for Janet.

It was a warm shade of amber, the same as Janet's eyes, and with a low neckline which felt very daring to Janet as she walked into the Rococo that evening.

"Don't hunch up!" Christabel whispered. "You confidently decided it was time for a change — right? And I confidently gave you one.

It really did something for my morale, too. Maybe I should go back to hairdressing!"

A slow excitement was beginning to rise in Janet. She felt as if this was her first date with Gerry, and was as shy as if she'd only just met him.

For this reason she drank more dinner wine than usual and laughed a lot. Jim danced with her several times, complimenting her on her appearance.

Halfway through the evening Christabel followed her to the powder room.

"Has Gerry said anything about your hair — or your dress? He seems very quiet tonight."

"I don't think he approves," Janet said, trying not to sound as bleak as she felt. "He's being so polite — as if he was seeing Cinderella for what she is without midnight having to strike."

Each time Janet caught sight of herself she felt a little thrill of delighted surprise. Oh, why couldn't Gerry be impressed, too?

But of course, she was no different inside. She couldn't change that, and the truth was that she wanted Gerry to love the Janet he'd always known, not some new glamorous version. So really, there was no way round the problem.

Towards midnight, she found herself drifting in a dreamy waltz in Gerry's arms.

"I suppose you'll be busy on Tuesday, again?" he asked.

"Busy?"

"Like this week? Were you with new friends you've made since Christy came along?"

Not knowing how to explain, she maintained a confused silence.

"Janet — is there someone else?"

For a moment, she thought she'd misunderstood him and stared at him, startled.

"I'm sorry — I didn't mean to pry, only . . . I just want to know . . . oh, Janet! Have I left it too late? I've been so blind all these years! We've always been so right together. Seeing you was like coming home, and I just took it for granted. Then last week when you said . . . Janet, please *say* something."

Perhaps someone more sophisticated would have kept him guessing, savouring the moment. But Janet couldn't bear the anxiety in his face, or contain the joy in her heart.

"There's no-one else. Only you, Gerry — always."

"Promise me you'll always be and look the same as you always have, darling Jan," he said tenderly.

He kissed the top of her head, then held her away to study her, as if something had just struck him. "Have you had your hair cut?"

Janet laughed aloud for pure joy.

"It's past midnight now," she said happily. "And not a pumpkin in sight!" □

MAN

Who would have believed that two people so different could have so much in common . . .

and BOY

Complete Story

by SARAH PARKES

D ONALD BANKS hardly noticed the boy who sat down beside him on the bus because all the other seats were taken.

Old Donald was too busy looking out of the window, watching anxiously for his stop. It seemed to him that all the old landmarks were going — there were new shops where the fire station had stood and the cinema was now a bingo hall.

The young lady from the council had kindly offered to come to his house, to save him the journey. But Donald didn't want the neighbours to know about her.

He had visited her three times now and his excitement grew with each journey. He took with him his little brown attaché-case. It was just the right size for his things.

He had bought it years ago for his daughter, Francie, when she had gone to the grammar school — inside the lid there was still the label with her name, "Frances Banks", and the address. Amy, his wife, had written it for her.

If Amy had been alive he would not have been doing this. Never!

Yet if she could see what he was doing she would be pleased; he was sure of that.

He looked out of the window, watching the streets of the town.

Beside him, the boy, Pete, fidgeted. He searched through his pockets hoping to find something to eat or, perhaps, something to play with. Unlike the old man, he had nowhere to go, nothing special to do.

T HE old man reacted to his restless movements. "Why aren't you at school?" he asked.

"Dentist." Pete had found this a useful excuse when he was playing truant from school.

Only last week a police-woman had stopped him, and when he had put his hand over his mouth and mumbled, "Dentist," she had been quite sympathetic.

No-one cared, really, whether he was at school or not. His mother hadn't much time for teachers as long as they didn't bother *her*.

MAN AND BOY

He had thought, when he had started at the new comprehensive, that it would be different. His mum had bought him all the uniform; there were new buildings with grass in between, a super sports field and the sun streaming into the art room.

But, after all, it was just like the junior school — everyone else seemed to know just what they were doing. All except him — he was still getting his classwork all wrong and never doing his homework. He wrote his name on the front of all the new books, and then — nothing more.

In the second year he had started fooling around. He could make the other boys laugh and annoy the teachers.

Then they had tired of him. They were working most of them, for exams or playing games seriously. They stopped laughing and said, "Oh, shut up!" when he tried to be funny.

That was when he had started staying away from school or slipping out after the register. No-one seemed to notice. Sometimes he even earned money doing odd jobs.

It was better than being at school where all the boys knew what they were doing, except for him. The only problem was finding something to pass the time.

THE old man stood up. "This is Skates Corner, isn't it? I must have gone past my stop."

Pete pulled his legs back to let the old man pass. Then as he slid over into the vacant window seat, he saw the little brown attaché-case. He looked round for the old man.

"Hey!" he shouted. But the old man was gone; the bus was moving on.

Pete fingered the shabby attaché-case — it was nothing to do with him. Then, suddenly, he thought, it'll be something to *do.*

He picked up the case and moved down to the door. He said to the driver, "The old man left his case on the seat." But the driver didn't hear him.

He got off the bus, meaning to run back to the old fellow. But now he realised that he was unlikely to find him. They were in the city centre and the streets were crowded with shoppers.

By the time he had walked back to Skates Corner, the old man would have been swallowed up in the afternoon crowds.

He shrugged off the problem and headed for home.

Pete let himself in to the empty flat. He put the case on the kitchen table and looked around for something to eat. He felt guilty with the case lying there in front of him. But his intentions had been good; he really had meant to run after the old chap and return it.

He felt guilty when he opened it.

He looked. He touched the things gently. He turned them over carefully.

THEN he sat down at the table and studied them — they were so *new*. And the pencil case was like a child's. It made him think, not of his Junior School, but of Infants long ago.

In those days it seemed the sun always shone, lighting up the fish tank, and the teachers had smiled and encouraged him, saying, "Try again, Peter."

He had loved going to school then. He was sorry when his mother said: "I'm not turning out in the cold today; you'll have to stay home from school."

Sometimes she went away and left him with his gran and so he would be away from school for days at a time. He had hated missing school in those days.

The things in the old man's case were like the things that he had had in the Infant classroom — the books were shiny with comic-clear drawings and clear round print.

They had tried to get him to read this sort of book, he remembered, for what they called Special tuition, but he had refused to look at what he called "Baby stuff".

Perhaps they belonged to the old man's grandchild. But why was he carrying them around, then? It was all very odd, Pete thought.

Much later, he was still sitting at the kitchen table, absorbed in the books. He didn't hear his mother come in.

"Will you please clear that stuff off the table," she said. "I want to get tea."

The boy gathered the books and papers together to protect them.

"Where did you get that case?" she asked.

He told her.

She glanced at the attaché-case and read off the faded label: "Frances Banks, 15 Marlborough Avenue. That's out Keys Common way — you'd better take it back after tea, Pete."

He waited until she went out again, then walked out to Keys Common because he had run out of money. It was dark when he got to Marlborough Avenue and rang the bell of number 15. He was still turning the whole thing over in his mind . . .

Donald Banks opened the door warily.

When he had got off the bus and realised that he had forgotten his case, he had stood on the pavement almost in tears. He had even stumbled after the bus for a moment, stupidly.

Then he had turned to go home. He didn't want to go to his lesson without his books and his pencil case — the young lady would think he was a fool.

She was such a nice girl, like Amy had been long ago.

When the doorbell had rung in the silence of the evening he had thought foolishly that it was *them* coming to ask, "Why did you miss your lesson, Mr Banks? Don't you want to learn how to read?"

But it was an untidy boy holding his case tightly to him.

Donald reached out, but the boy kept hold of it. "Is your name Banks?"

When Donald nodded, the boy said, "You forgot your grand-daughter's case."

"It's *my* case. Where did you get it from?" But even as Donald spoke he began to remember that a boy had sat beside him on the bus.

He watched the boy's puzzled expression. Then, suddenly, the youngster's face lit up with realisation.

"Can't you read, Mr Banks?" he blurted out.

"You've been opening my case," Donald said angrily.

"Those books in there — they're for learning to read!"

"Well?" But the anger had gone from Donald's voice. He could feel the intensity, the great effort that the boy was making. He waited.

"You're ever so old."

Donald Banks still waited, patient now. He was remembering, all those years back, how Francie had struggled at times to find the right words to ask the right questions. He had been patient with her.

And all the years he had hidden from her, with Amy's help, the fact that her old dad couldn't read.

"I would have thought you were too old to learn," the boy said, but he didn't mean to be rude."I can write my name of course — it's Peter — and lots of words. Long words like geography even, and changing-rooms and September. Words like that I can read. But I can't read a book or even a comic or what's on a record sleeve . . ."

Then he held out the case. There wasn't any more to say. He turned to go.

"You can come in," Donald Banks said. "I'm having my tea. The old woman next door made me a pie, but it's too big for me. You can have a piece."

He held open the door and Pete followed him into the kitchen.

"I can't read books," Donald said. "Not even the paper. But I'm going to. And a boy like you could do it, too.

"But first of all you'd better phone your mum and let her know where you are."

He opened the case. "I'll show you. This is how I began two or three weeks back. I wasn't too proud to begin . . . "

"I could do it?" Pete asked. Then, with conviction: "I could do it." □

The Monarch Of The Glen

Ruadh, the headstrong young roe deer, learns his lessons the hard way, but soon establishes himself as a true Monarch of the Glen.

Gideon's WAY

By GIDEON SCOTT MAY

THERE'S a "royal" roebuck on Croft Douglas, a truly handsome creature who, this year, has been crowned with a full set of ivory-tipped antlers.

He was born and bred here and had a twin sister, which was a blessing for his mother because the sister stuck faithfully to her mother's side, obediently following all her instructions, while Ruadh, as we called him, turned out to be a real terror and was a sore trial to his mother.

He paid not the slightest attention to her pleas for better behaviour and her repeated warnings not to walk the Forestry lands on the hill.

Ruadh continued to turn a deaf ear to all this good advice until he came face to face with a big dog fox. It would be hard to say which was the more surprised, but, luckily, the fox was handicapped by a blue mountain hare already clasped in its jaws.

For the first time in his life, Ruadh was really frightened and, spinning

quickly around, bounded back to the safety of his mother's side.

The next time he got into trouble was when taking one of his "I wonder where this leads to" walks. He failed to see a wild cat crouching on a crag of rock just above him.

The cat had two hungry kittens in her den, and was hunting for food. Hardly believing her good luck, she launched an attack like a charging lioness.

Fortunately, Ruadh's mother had been looking for him and fought the wild cat with her flailing, flint-sharp forefeet, until it gave a last half-hearted snarl and fled.

Ruadh had got the fright of his young life and, in the days to come, stayed, like his sister, dutifully by his mother's side.

SOME time later, he was about to take a drink in a placid woodland pool when he caught sight of his own reflection, complete with two spiky horns on his head.

Delighted, he tore the moss off the trees· with them, dug up the earth and scattered the molehills with rumbling growls of satisfaction.

He was a force to be reckoned with now and no longer feared the fangs of the fox or sharp claws of the wild cat.

One misty, midsummer morning, the wanderlust came over him again so, once more, he left the safety of his home in the hazel woods and stepped boldly in to the outside world. He was unafraid, confident that his brand-new armament of antlers could meet any challenge.

But the deadliest danger, unbeknown to Ruadh, lay hidden in the Forestry lands on the hill — headhunters with automatic rifles topped with telescopic sights, who had paid for the privilege of gaining a head such as his.

Some sixth-sense saved Ruadh and he spun round just as a rifle spat, then escaped through the spruce thickets, limping home with a bullet wound in his hind leg.

But Ruadh didn't waste any time feeling sorry for himself. He was made of sterner stuff and sensibly rested himself until his wound had healed.

Having learned his lesson, he decided to make this comparatively safe stretch of Strathtummel his home. Meticulously, he marked the area of ground he claimed as his own by spraying his boundary lines with musk that held an invitation for passing females, but also a wordless warning for wandering males.

A LADY called at Croft Douglas asking permission to paint the view from our land. I offered to conduct her to what I thought was the best painting vantage point, but the lady independently said she would like to pick her own and set off with all her artistic accoutrements.

About half an hour later, just as we were sitting down to dinner, there was a tremendous hammering at the front door. It was the artist lady, distraught and dishevelled, gasping almost hysterically.

"A huge beast, with a great granite body, black face and eyes glowing like red-hot coals, came charging and roaring at me! It was absolutely terrifying!"

I couldn't believe that such a thing could happen in our peaceful Strathtummel but, just the same, I snatched a stout stick from its resting place in the porch and set out to investigate.

I had no difficulty at all in locating the spot the lady had selected. An easel lay in a patch of bracken with one leg raised pathetically as a signal for help, a palette daubed with paint hung from a hazel tree branch like some exotic bloom, and brushes were strewn around in a colourful circle like broken branch twigs after a storm.

Suddenly, a fearsome face with fire-flecked eyes bobbed up behind a huge boulder, with a roar that made the hairs stand up on the back of my neck.

After I had recovered from my initial shock, I recognised the "monster" — it was Ruadh. He had burnished his antlers on silver birch bark and dipped his head into a black peat bog.

As he, almost apologetically, washed his face on a big, wet sponge of sphagnum moss, I told him how wrong it was to go around scaring the life out of people like that.

And yet I knew Ruadh was right. He had found the ideal way to defend his territory and frighten off the other big bucks without any fighting.

I went back to the woods that evening to have another word with Ruadh. I felt I had to tell him, as his friend, that I understood.

I saw Ruadh first. He was standing under a spangled veil of silver birch leaves, happily whispering sweet nothings into the delicate ear of a dainty doe, so I quietly turned around and slipped away, unnoticed. □

I Wish... How I Wish...

**The story of
a little girl's first
encounter with
grief —
and her headlong
race back
to the joy
of living.**

L UCY led the way importantly into the toy department. My daughter, aged seven, nearly eight, was already staking her claim for a birthday present in a few weeks' time. Lucy was just like her father — she knew what she wanted and was determined to get it.

The toy department was hot, and already Lucy had disappeared. Then suddenly I saw her, talking earnestly to a saleslady in a black dress. I hurried over.

"But they were here last week!" Lucy was saying, and the saleslady turned to me with relief.

Complete Story by

ELIZABETH ASHCROFT

I WISH ... HOW I WISH ...

"I'm sorry," she said, "but we're coming up to Sales, and our normal range is being put aside while we get out the Sale goods."

"But I want to see them now!" Lucy persisted, and we both sighed.

"The dolls' houses are round the corner," the saleslady said. "They are not being reduced in the Sale."

Dolls' houses? Lucy, the tomboy who was pestering me to let her have riding lessons? I blinked. Lucy was smiling eagerly, and gasped with delight when we came upon the dolls' houses.

They were in two neat rows. Lucy hung over them raptly, admiring the most expensive looking.

I glanced furtively at the price tag.

"Lucy, do you know how much this one is?"

"No." She turned innocent blue eyes to me. "Isn't it absolutely fabulous, Mummy?"

A fabulous price, I thought grimly. I could just see my husband's face if I announced blithely I'd just spent £62.34 on a doll's house.

"Isn't there anything cheaper?" I asked weakly.

"Not like this one," Lucy explained carefully. "This is special. Didn't you have a doll's house when you were little, Mummy? This is just what I'd like to live in, when I grow up."

And suddenly, looking down at the exquisitely-made doll's house, I remembered.

Remembered when I was Lucy's age, and living with my grandparents, because my parents had died in a car crash. When the only thing I wanted in life was a doll's house. And Mary next door had one, and didn't even play with it. I'd begun to realise the bitter unfairness of life.

Mary had everything. A mother and father, a baby sister, brothers, a dog, and a doll's house. All I had were Grandma and Grandpa, who didn't even seem to like me very much . . .

I HAD been seven when I went to live with them in their neat, scrubbed, little house on the edge of the village green. After the town, the nights were so dark and quiet that I was frightened. Grandma wouldn't even let me have a nightlight to keep me company.

I hated the silence, the great, empty, green fields, and the village which only came to life when the bus called twice a day. Grandpa only worked part time, because he had a bad chest, and the rest of the time he spent in the garden, or looking after his hens.

When I arrived, still shocked from the loss of my parents, Grandpa informed me gruffly that the hens were to be my job.

I stared at him blankly. I didn't know anything about hens, and didn't want to.

He glared down at me from beneath bushy, white eyebrows.

"Feed them, child, every day. And collect the eggs and bring them to your grandmother before you go to school. And never, never, leave the gate to the run open. You understand?"

Grandpa towered over me. He wasn't a bit like my gentle father, who'd been a teacher, and dreamy like me.

The first morning, I crept out to the hen run and stared in. Ten hens, there were, with pecking yellow beaks and scratching busy claws. Then the cockerel came strutting round the corner of the chicken house, and I'd never seen anything so ferocious looking. Then I smelled the already familiar tobacco which meant Grandpa was there.

"Go on," he said impatiently, putting the bucket into my nerveless hands. "In you go." And he pushed me in and shut the gate on me.

Petrified, I flung the seed all over the ground and ran to the nesting boxes. The hens were all round me. I could feel their bodies brushing my bare legs. I began to shake.

"Open the boxes!" Grandpa said impatiently. "Go on, child! If you're going to do a job, do it properly!"

Gingerly I opened the boxes and took the eggs off the nests, marvelling at their warmth, the way little bits of straw stuck to them. I put eight eggs carefully in the bowl, turned, and saw the cockerel coming towards me, his wings outstretched, his yellow beak wide.

"He's going to bite me!" I screamed, and promptly dropped the bowl. The eggs fell in a messy scramble of yellow and white and bits of shell on to the grass, and Grandpa let out a bellow of anguish.

"You stupid child! Can't you do anything right?"

That was the first and last time he let me collect the eggs, and I was sure he'd never forgive me. But I learned that day that Grandpa's favourite saying was *Do a job, and do it properly.* Nothing he ever asked me to do got done properly, because I was so scared of him.

At home, my parents had called me Adeline, or Linny. Grandma called me Addie, and Grandpa never called me anything. He and Grandma spoke with a Kentish burr which was oddly peaceful after the quick London accent, and soon I became accustomed to it and even spoke with a soft burr myself.

Grandpa continued to ignore me. He didn't like me, and I didn't know why.

Once I asked Grandma if I could have piano lessons.

"Piano lessons?" He looked at me as though I were mad, then spoke gruffly to Gran. "What nonsense are you stuffing the child's head with? She could be outside, learning our country ways."

"I asked Gran!" I blurted out defiantly, voice wobbling. "Mary next door has them. She can play 'The Blue Danube.' "

Grandpa gave a little bark of something suspiciously like laughter.

"And what good is that going to do her when she's left school?

And how is your schooling getting along? Last time I saw your teacher, he said you were behind in your arithmetic and geography and you weren't even trying. You stick to your books, my girl, and study hard."

Trust Grandpa, always damping down my little enthusiasms.

Then Mary was given the doll's house and when I saw it, it was like coming home.

It was just like our house had been in London. A little cosy kitchen, and a sitting-room with comfy, stuffed chairs and chintzy curtains. One little bedroom was even furnished like mine had been, all pink and frilly.

Not like my room now, with the plain, slippery, wooden floor which creaked, the thin curtains, and narrow brass bedstead in which I could never get comfortable.

I wasn't sturdy and red faced and lively, but fair and pale, and I caught colds. I disappointed my grandparents.

Longing to return to the home that wasn't there any more, I adored that doll's house. And when Mary, after a few weeks, abandoned it, I couldn't understand her.

"Don't you like it?" I asked her blankly.

"Not much," Mary said briefly. "I'd rather *do* something." And she disappeared with her brothers, leaving me alone with the doll's house, blissful and envious.

In Mary's large, noisy family there were crumpets cooked over the roaring fire for tea. Grandma didn't hold with such things. You ate bread as the good Lord had intended you to; as she made it, wholesome and brown, with a knob of butter on it.

AFTER I'd been with Grandma and Grandpa for six months, Grandma suddenly realised my birthday was coming up. "You'll be eight soon, Addie?" She'd relented a little lately, begun giving me little treats, like jam on my bread and butter for tea.

I nodded importantly. Eight was an enormous, advanced age.

But Grandpa damped my sudden enthusiasm.

"Child," he said gruffly, "this morning you left the gate open after you fed the hens."

I blinked apprehensively. It was only that week that I'd dared to venture into the hen run, and found to my astonishment that the hens were friends after all.

"Seven hens I had to catch," Grandpa went on inexorably. "And nowhere could I find you to help me. Off playing with that Mary, were you?"

"I was — p-playing with her doll's house," I stammered.

Grandpa's eyes hardened. He looked fiercer than ever.

"Doll's house!" he grunted. "No pocket money for a week, to remind you that if a thing's worth doing it's worth doing properly."

How tired I was growing of that phrase!

"Can't you find anything better to do? Doll's house!" he snorted.

Suddenly, from somewhere, I found courage. "I like dolls' houses," I stated firmly. "Grandma, could I have a doll's house for my birthday? That's all I want, really."

At home, my parents had always asked me what I wanted, to make sure I wasn't disappointed. Suddenly, remembering them, wrenched with sorrow for them, tears sprang to my eyes, and Grandpa snorted again.

"Want!" he said. "You want a present for your birthday? What you want and what you'll get are two different things, my girl."

I sat there with tears trickling down my cheeks, and Grandma looked at me with a measure of sympathy.

"We can't afford dolls' houses, Addie," she said. "Expensive, they are. Mary's must have cost a fortune. It's even got an electric fire, I see."

I GAZED at her, open mouthed. Grandma had seen the doll's house? She looked embarrassed. "Her ma showed me when she bought it. Now, get on with your meal and no more tears. Your grandpa doesn't like tears."

Grandpa didn't like me, I thought mournfully. He wished I'd been a boy. My father had been the apple of his eye. When he had been killed, Grandpa shut himself in his shed at the bottom of the garden for a week, refusing to come out except to go to bed.

Grandma told me how she even took his meals down to him.

Sometimes now he would sit there, on a creaking old chair, surveying his neat rows of lettuces and cabbages, all marching into the distance like an army; the berries reddening like jewels, and the strawberries with scraps of paper strung along on cotton to frighten the birds. Stern, unapproachable, he would look at me unseeingly, and I'd creep away.

But all I could think about was the doll's house. I dreamed achingly about it when I was at school, and I played with it in Mary's bedroom when she was out. Then, one day, her mother appeared with a mug of lemonade for me.

"You love that doll's house, don't you, Addie?"

Sprawled on the floor, I nodded raptly.

"Would you like it?" she asked abruptly, and suddenly my heart was in my mouth. I sat up on Mary's pale blue rug, and stared at her.

"Like it?" I stammered, overwhelmed.

"Mary never plays with it. It's such a pity to keep it here when you're the one who plays with it all the time. Mary tells me it's your birthday soon, and if you'd like it, she'd give it to you."

I couldn't believe it. The doll's house was mine! I could take it back to Grandma's and play with it, and pretend I was home again, with my parents, where I was happy and loved, not just tolerated, as I was at Gran's.

I staggered jubilantly across the lane and into Grandma's kitchen, clutching the doll's house in my arms. It was heavy, and bits of the roof were sticking into my chest, but I didn't care. In a bag under my arm I had all the furniture, all ready to be put into the right rooms.

Suddenly, for the first time since I'd come to the village, I was truly happy.

But Grandpa was there. He looked up with a frown from the daily paper.

"Addie! Whatever have you got there?" Grandma's voice was startled, apprehensive.

"A doll's house!" I blurted out raptly. "Mary's mother gave it to me! It's mine! Mary doesn't want it, and isn't it lovely! Look at it, Grandma!"

I put it on the table, and never realised how silent the room had become. Grandma was holding her breath, and Grandpa got up coughing. It was one of his bad days, I could see, and suddenly I was filled with terror.

"You can take that back, right this minute," he said flatly.

I didn't believe him.

"Take it back? I can't! It's mine!" I said, backing away.

"You'll take it back right now!" he boomed. "I'll not have my granddaughter accepting charity from anyone."

I didn't know what he was talking about. "But Mary doesn't want it."

Grandma reached across and took it from me. The little windows swung open emptily and the door flew open. I'd lost it before I'd ever owned it.

"But it's a present!" I wailed. "Grandpa, it's my birthday present."

"Been telling them what *you* want, again, have you?" He stamped out, and I burst into tears and rushed up to my little room.

They didn't understand, they'd never understand. They were cold, unloving. I could have played with the doll's house for hours, on my own.

I put my hand under the skimpy eiderdown and bawled.

That evening, I ran away. I packed my suitcase and stuffed my few favourite possessions into it. Then I crept out into the June night. It was dark and warm, and overhead something hooted eerily. I tried not to scream. I'd never been out so late at night, alone.

I stood at the little white gate and looked back at the neat house. Every window shone in the moonlight, and up the path marched a row of upright standard roses, Grandpa's only concession to Grandma's love of flowers.

Suddenly, I wished I was back in my bed, hard though it was. Then I remembered the doll's house and sniffed miserably, and marched off down the road.

An hour later I was sitting at the side of a ditch, covered in dust and grass, blood running down my leg, tears streaming down my dirty cheeks. A car had come round the corner and caught me as I dodged out of the way.

The driver, a pale young man, was frantic.

"It wasn't my fault!" he kept saying. "I didn't even see you. Have you hurt yourself badly? Poor little kid."

I wiped dust out of my eyes, rubbed my leg, which was hurting, said, "I want my gran," and fainted.

THE next thing I remembered, I was in hospital. I'd had concussion and a broken leg and bruises, and Gran was sitting by my bed anxiously.

I opened my eyes groggily, and suddenly an unfamiliar smile flitted across Grandma's face.

"Addie. Addie, dear, do you feel better?" Her thin hand was warm on my forehead, then, for the first time, she was kissing me.

"Oh, Grandma, I was so miserable," I said weakly.

"If you ran away you must have been, dear. We figured that out for ourselves." There was a touch of amusement in her voice, then her arms were round me and I was crying on her shoulder. It would be all right now, I thought thankfully. They'd forgiven me.

But Grandpa didn't seem to have forgiven me at all. When I arrived home he just looked over the top of his paper at me and grunted.

"That was a silly thing to do. If you set out to do a thing, do it properly, or not at all. Don't get yourself run over."

Next day he began shutting himself up in his shed, the way he had when my father was killed. He kept the door locked, and Grandma grew pale faced and worried.

Once I heard a great knocking and a crash from the shed. Grandma ran out, then came back quietly, her face thoughtful.

She made some currant buns, and we sat at the kitchen table eating them, warm and spicy from the oven. For the first time, I felt at home. If only Grandpa liked me . . .

What with the accident, I clean forgot my birthday, till the morning Mary poked her head into the kitchen.

I WISH ... HOW I WISH ...

"I brought you a card, Addie," she said. "And a present." She flashed a defiant glance at Grandpa, who, to my surprise, went a little red.

"It's a new dress. Ma and I bought it in the market."

It was a pretty dress, pink and feminine, and I loved it.

Then Grandma brought out a little parcel, tied with yellow ribbon, from behind the old wooden clock on the mantelpiece.

"There, Addie," she said. "That was your dad's, when he was little. I always kept it for his son, but he never had one, so you'd better have it instead."

Eagerly, I undid the paper. It was a boy's watch, with a wide, black strap, and it fitted me perfectly.

"Oh, Gran, it's lovely. I'll wear it always," I said, and was horrified to see a tear slipping down her nose.

She coughed loudly, then got up and began to clear the table.

Grandpa pushed his chair back with a rasping squeak and went out. He hadn't even said Happy Birthday. But then the door opened and he stumped in again, bearing a huge, unwieldy parcel, wrapped untidily in crumpled brown paper.

"There you are," he said gruffly. "That's what you wanted. Now you've got it, you be satisfied."

Mystified, I tore off the wrapping, and stared astonished at a doll's house. A doll's house which leaned a little sideways, and had a crooked front door, and swung open on its hinges. It had mock beams across the ceilings and was painted to resemble a country cottage, even with a little wooden fireplace. It was beautiful and strange and funny, and I loved it at first sight.

"Oh, Grandpa!" I gasped finally. "It's lovely! It's absolutely lovely!"

"Not perfect," he said disapprovingly. "But the best I could do."

I gazed at him wide eyed. Grandpa, admitting something he'd done wasn't perfect?

And suddenly I knew. That's what he'd been doing, hidden away in his shed.

"You made it, Grandpa? You mean you really made it, specially for me?"

He nodded. "Can't have you running away just because you don't have a doll's house. Fool thing to run away for. You want a real reason for doing something like that."

Then I realised what I should have known a long time ago. Grandpa wasn't good with words. He was good with his hands, and making things grow, but not with words.

And I realised something else. He'd spent hours shut in his shed, making the doll's house, because he cared for me. He must, or he wouldn't have bothered.

"Oh, Grandpa, I love it," I said shyly. "It's better than Mary's. It's — real looking." It was, too. It looked, somehow, lived in, and loved. A home, not a shop-bought toy.

"Right, Addie." He began to put on his big, clumpy shoes. "Time to feed the hens. And don't forget to shut the gate."

He'd called me Addie. For the first time, Grandpa had given me a name.

"Get on with it, you two," Grandma said. "And I'll have some cocoa for you both when you come back."

Going out to the hen-house, brimming with happiness, I tripped, and Grandpa's strong hand came out to catch me. We walked hand in hand to feed the hens, together . . .

Now, looking at Lucy's eager face in the toy department, I remembered Gran and Gramp, and the love in that small house in the country.

I hadn't been old enough to realise, those first few months, that they were both numb with grief, especially Gramp. They weren't used to small girls, after just rearing one small boy, and that a long time ago.

I'd lived with them till I married, and when they died they left me the house, where we still went for holidays and weekends. It was still home to me.

Lucy, I decided, would have to know the truth.

"Lucy, love," I began firmly. "We can't possibly afford a doll's house like that. It's much too expensive."

"Oh, I don't want that one," she assured me blithely. "I just brought you to show you what I want. I thought Daddy could make it. He likes making things. And he could make one like that, couldn't he, Mummy?"

Suddenly I was laughing out loud, and the saleslady looked at me, surprised.

My devious daughter, I thought. She'd known all along how to get round me. Adam, my husband, did love making things, shutting himself in the toolshed at the bottom of the garden.

In the lift to the ground floor Lucy leaned against me, sagging, suddenly tired. I was filled with an odd contentment. Lucy, at least, had never been lonely or unhappy, as I was at her age.

And Adam, I knew, would make Lucy's doll's house. With love, as my grandfather had made mine. □

157

IN A

The first little lie was the hardest — the next came much more easily.

A FTER a last check on the meagre contents of her suitcase, Emily Jane closed the lid and slipped the catches home. She glanced at her watch and saw there was just time for a cup of tea.

Sitting at the table in her bright kitchen, she studied for the last time the itinerary for the coach trip. Then, very resolutely, she tore the glossy paper into tiny shreds and dropped them into the bin.

Tabby, her cat, was out somewhere, and Emily Jane hoped she wouldn't appear to rub herself sorrowfully against her legs, before she could get away.

John and Muriel, her son and daughter-in-law, had offered to take Tabby, but it seemed more sensible to leave her in her own territory and have Mabel from next door come in to feed her.

GOOD CAUSE

The taxi arrived, and soon she was speeding past the coach terminal in town. She saw two gleaming white coaches waiting to set off on their journey north.

"Scotland's glorious in the summer, Mum," John had said. "Can't think of a better tonic after the long hard winter."

"But that fortnight, John? Isn't that about the time Muriel should be having the baby . . . ?" Her voice had faded away, afraid that by actually voicing it, things might go wrong again, even at this late stage.

John had laughed with a confidence she didn't share.

"Oh, give or take a couple of weeks. Besides, you'd only be sitting at home worrying. You know what Muriel's mother is. She insists she's going to be there, so you'd be better coming after she's gone."

So Emily Jane had been persuaded and the holiday booked. She cancelled her milk and her papers, arranged with Mabel to feed Tabby, and even booked to have her hair permed.

As she might be difficult to contact on a touring holiday, she'd told

159

John she'd phone him — every couple of days or so — just in case there was any news.

Then the card from the hospital had arrived and thrown Emily Jane into a panic. Of course she'd known she was to go in sometime for her gall bladder trouble, but it was the timing of it which was so appalling.

However, half an hour and two cups of tea later, she knew what she must do . . .

"All admissions go in this way, lady." The taxi driver's voice broke into her thoughts as he brought the vehicle to a standstill.

Opening the car door, he offered her a helping hand.

"Thank you," she said graciously. "I can manage. If you would just be good enough to bring my case."

The admission clerk was most helpful and welcoming.

"Mrs Wood, isn't it? Take a seat. I've got your case notes here, dear. Just a few things to check."

"That's right," Emily Jane replied, when the clerk read out her address and phone number.

"Now, that just leaves 'next of kin'." She was reading the next line down. "John Wood . . . Headley 2640?" She looked up questioningly.

"No!" Emily Jane said, fear in her voice.

"I'm sorry." The clerk was concerned not to upset this new patient. Family rifts were not uncommon to her. "Is there someone else you'd rather . . . ?"

"No!" Emily Jane replied hastily. She hadn't thought of this. She put a hand to her head. "If I could just have a cup of tea."

"Of course. Just a minute."

The clerk left her sitting at the desk, and crossed the large reception area to a drinks dispensing machine.

"That's better," Emily Jane said, sipping the sweet tea. "Helps me think straight. Yes, John Wood is correct. He's my only son." She said it with pride.

The clerk bent her head over the desk, and Emily Jane detected the smile as she said, "Right. That just about completes it."

"He can't be contacted, though," Emily Jane added quickly. "He and his wife are away on holiday. If you would just make a note of that." She watched the young woman, surprised at how calmly she'd told the lie.

"Oh, that's all right," the clerk replied. "It's only a formality and would only be used in an absolute emergency. Pity he's had to take his holiday while you're here. Have you got their holiday address?"

"No. They're touring." Then leaping to her son's defence: "He'd no choice about going. His firm sent him. A sort of working holiday."

Emily Jane put a hand over her mouth, shocked at the ease with which one lie could follow another.

The ward was one of the long Nightingale type. She was pleased about that; she'd not have been happy away from the nurses in that four-bedded ward.

"Now, Mrs Wood." It was Sister in her green dress and white frilly cap. "You'll have your operation tomorrow. Because of the heart attack two years ago, Doctor will want to do a tracing of your heart. He'll want to listen in, take some blood and ask you all sorts of questions. OK?"

"Yes. That's all right, Sister." She smiled and looked up at the stream of visitors coming through the door.

"Remember to tell your relatives, no visiting on operation day. But they can phone, of course." Sister was away down the ward before Emily Jane could reply.

JUST give you a wash and sit you up before visiting, Mrs Wood." Two young nurses were at her bedside and pulling the screens. "Is it that time already?" Emily Jane tried to raise herself. "Oh! That's sore."

"Bound to be, love. You only had your operation yesterday."

Emily Jane had lost a day and a half and had only vague memories of waking from a drugged sleep.

"No, I shan't be having any visitors," she said in answer to the nurse's question.

"Oh. That's a shame," the young nurse said sympathetically.

"I've only one son and he's away at present," Emily Jane replied calmly.

She could feel rather than see the expression that passed between the two girls. How could they begin to understand?

From her new vantage point propped up on pillows, Emily Jane stole a glance round the ward. All the beds she could see had one or more visitors beside them, and there was a low hum of conversation. A young man came rushing through the door just then and hurried over to a bed halfway up the ward.

Something about the way he walked reminded her of John and she remembered again that last time he'd had to visit her in hospital.

John and Muriel had both come for the first few days. Emily Jane had been so poorly at first, she didn't remember too much about it, but they'd seemed to be there for most of the time.

Until the day John had come alone and his mother had known immediately that something was wrong. He'd tried to fob her off, but she'd known. She'd guessed long before they actually told her.

Muriel had had yet another miscarriage — and her nearly too old to be having babies at all. So Emily had begun to think her John would never be a father.

As for herself, she so much wanted to be a granny. Worse than that — she felt she'd been to blame for Muriel's miscarriage. If she hadn't had a heart attack, Muriel wouldn't have had all that rushing

L

about, then maybe everything would have been all right.

"There you are. A nice cup of tea and a magazine." The young nurse spoke quietly. "Better than noisy visitors, eh?" She grinned mischievously.

The sweet tea was like nectarine and its warmth brought life flooding back through Emily Jane.

"Nurse!" she called softly to the one passing her bed. "Could I use the phone, please?"

"Of course. I'll get it for you."

Moments later Emily Jane held her breath while she waited for the ringing to stop. As it did she pushed the coins in and began.

"John! Mum here. How's things? Any news?"

"Mum! Everything's great. How are you?"

"I'm fine. What about Muriel?"

"Nothing to report, yet. How's the holiday? OK?"

Emily Jane found her mouth had dried up. She could hardly get the words out. "Yes, everything's lovely, John." It wasn't so easy to lie to her son.

Then the pips were going. She had more coins ready — just in case — but she didn't think she could prolong the deceit.

"Give my love to Muriel," she said. "I'll phone again in a couple of days."

Then the line went dead. She closed her eyes, still clutching the phone. Her heart was thumping up in her throat. It hadn't been as easy as she'd hoped. Yet she knew it had to be this way. She couldn't have those two worried about her. Not just now, anyway.

Her condition improved steadily over the next day or two, and she began taking a little food and sitting out of bed.

"The way you're progressing," Sister said, "you could be home in ten days."

EMILY JANE smiled, then bit her lip. How was she going to get out of that? Mabel from next door would be sure to smell a rat if she arrived home early, even if she managed to walk up straight. If Mabel found out, she'd fuss and insist on phoning John, which would be all right if everything was over — one way or another.

Thinking of John, she wasn't looking forward one bit to phoning him this evening. To have reassuring news of Muriel was vital, but to deceive her son — well, that was proving the hardest thing of all.

Just then, a porter entered the ward and went over to Sister, who was busy attending a patient opposite. He carried two large sprays of flowers, Cellophane-wrapped and tied with bows of ribbon.

After a few words with Sister, he came towards Emily Jane and, much to her amazement, placed one of the sprays on her bed.

"A bouquet for you, flower," he said cheerily, and went off whistling.

There had to be some mistake. No-one knew she was here.

She fingered the attached card, and had to wait for the mistiness to clear from her eyes before she could read.

To celebrate the safe delivery of Emma Jane.

Didn't they know she was Emily Jane? How careless to make such a mistake and cause such disappointment — and what a strange message.

It was at this point that she turned the card over. *To Granny Wood*, it said, and suddenly realisation began to dawn. But how . . . ?

Her thoughts were all confused, like an orchestra out of tune.

"You wanted the phone, Mrs Wood." It was her young nurse, wheeling the portable phone to her bedside.

She had the change ready on her locker top and with shaking hands began dialling the familiar number.

"You won't be needing that," a warm, familiar voice said, and a large, capable hand took the receiver from her.

"John! How? What . . . ?"

He stopped and held her head against his broad chest. "Oh, Mum," he whispered. "That you should go through all this alone. Just for us."

Hardly daring to speak, she asked, "Muriel . . . ?"

"Muriel's marvellous. Emma Jane arrived this morning, and she is *the* most beautiful baby."

John's voice was full of wonder and love. Taking his mother's hands in his, he searched her face.

"But how are you? It's been so difficult staying away since I . . ."

How long had he known and how? Emily wondered. Then suddenly none of that mattered. Emily Jane Wood was a granny. She wanted to shout it out for the whole ward to hear.

Instead, in a very controlled voice, she heard herself say:

"How did you find out I was here, son?"

"Oh, Mum, I became suspicious the night before you were due to leave, when you phoned saying not to expect any postcards. When I checked with the tour operators I found out you'd cancelled."

"Go on," she said quietly.

"Then when I went round to check your house . . . you remember I have a key?" He smiled and squeezed her hand affectionately. "The hospital card was on the table. After that it was easy — but I asked them not to tell you I'd phoned."

"And . . . Muriel?"

"I didn't tell her. Not until today." He moved the flowers and sat comfortably on the bed. "You know, Mum, I once remember Dad saying you never could keep a secret."

"He used to say the same of you, John." Emily Jane wiped tears of happiness from her face. "I think today he'd be proud of us both." □

© Frances Fitzgibbon 1980.

Complete Story by SARAH BURKHILL

TO HAVE AND TO HOLD

A bright new future beckoned him — but first he had to make his peace with the past.

IT'S a long time since I've been in the park. After you went away, Annie, I moved to the other side of the city, and there was never any reason to come back here.

At this time in the morning it's quiet, of course. Later on the children will come, to have a game of football, or play on the swings, or just run laughing over the grass with the dogs at their heels, barking excitedly.

But not at this time. Now it is peaceful, with only the distant drone of a grass-cutting machine and the song of birds.

The birds have been in full cry since half past six this morning. I know the time exactly because I heard the first shrill notes with the breaking dawn, and I checked the alarm clock at my bedside. Each day this week they've started later than the morning before, proof that winter is just around the corner.

The coming season is apparent in the reds and golds that surround me as I walk down the wide drive to the pond.

The colours were summer ones that day I first saw you, Annie. Yet today the sun is shining so strongly that I can easily believe it is that summer day again.

You brought so many new colours into my life from that first morning I met you here.

There are eight ducks on the pond today, funny, laughable little creatures, the kind with the green heads that you always liked. Three of them come paddling hopefully to the edge, but they realise I have nothing for them and swim off.

It's funny to think I would never have met you at all if that stone hadn't bounced up from the roadway on Friday night and cracked the side window of my car. But it did, and the next morning I drove to the garage in Victoria Street for a replacement, and killed the hour I

had to wait by walking in the park across the road.

It was the little girl who drew my attention to the ducks — she was laughing delightedly and pointing, so that I stopped and looked, too. Then I looked at the young woman who was with her, and you smiled and offered me some bread to throw.

I smiled back and started to shake my head but something changed my mind and I could feel my polite smile widen to a grin.

And do you know something, Annie? I didn't feel the least bit silly standing there chucking bread in the water and listening to the little girl's chatter.

I felt I ought to feel silly — twenty-nine-year-old Neil Harris, feeding the ducks for the first time in a quarter of a century. But with you it seemed . . . well, it seemed right.

I can't recall much of what I said that morning. Very little, probably. Small talk with strangers never was a strong point of mine.

My silence didn't matter, though. You did most of the talking — about the ducks and the weather and how you brought your niece, Karen, to the park most Saturday mornings, to give your sister-in-law a break.

In fact, you talked so easily and so animatedly that I was reluctant to leave and collect my car when the time came.

It had been a pleasant, relaxing hour, and the rest of the day was brightened by the thought of a young woman in jeans and a sweatshirt, her brown eyes shining and her hair done in plaits that stuck out at a ridiculous angle.

PROBABLY I knew right away that I wanted to see you again, but it wasn't until Thursday that I admitted it to myself, and tried to think up excuses for being in the park next Saturday. I didn't need them, of course. You and Karen greeted me like an old friend and my carefully-contrived lies remained unspoken.

That was a good day that second Saturday.

When the ducks had been duly fed, we went to the children's corner, so Karen could have a go on the chute. You were a little nervous about her climbing up alone, so I went up with her and you caught her at the bottom.

How absurd I must have looked! I couldn't understand what you were laughing at, until I looked round and saw the queue of children on the steps behind me.

Remember the cheeky-faced little lad with the deep voice. "Hurry up, mister. We all want a go!"

Faced with the glaring crowd, I took the quick way down, earning myself a cheer from you and Karen, and a suspicious look from an old lady walking her dog.

After that undignified descent, I suggested we all go to the café across the road for a cold drink.

"But it's much too nice to be inside!" you protested. "Let's just get something from the kiosk, shall we?"

So we bought ice lollies and walked through the rockery garden eating them, orange rims round our mouths.

You kept the stick from your lolly and wrote our names and the date on it. You liked to have something to remind you of nice times, you told me, and the stick would be a small memento.

I couldn't help laughing then, and you laughed with me so that it was easy to ask you out that night.

Afterwards, when I took you home and you said how much you had enjoyed it, I realised you had no "memento." But you just touched your lips where I had kissed you, and said you didn't need one.

The rest of that year went by in a jumble of new, shared experiences.

The long, lazy summer when we explored every inch of that park, our special place, and you made me carve our initials on an old dead tree stump.

Then the autumn and the lengthening nights when we sought out quiet country pubs for dinner, and collected pine cones and leaves in the woods, for you to use later for Christmas decorations.

Even the winter, a season I had never liked, was different when I spent it with you, making plans for our future, dreaming dreams together.

W E were married in March, on a cold day when the sun tried valiantly to get through but didn't quite make it.

But it didn't matter to me, because the sun was no longer the centre of my particular universe.

It was difficult to believe I hadn't known you for ever, but in truth it was less than a year since a little girl had said: "Hello, I'm Karen and this is my Aunt Annie."

Annie, Annie, Annie. In the early days I would say the two syllables aloud, over and over again, like a child repeating a newly-learned word. Annie. My whole world in five little letters.

Sometimes, when you were pottering about our flat, I used just to watch you, unable to believe that you were mine.

"What are you thinking?" you always asked, if you looked up and caught me.

"Nothing," I would reply, smiling stupidly.

But you knew. You always knew, in spite of the difficulty I had with words, the feelings I couldn't express properly.

There were no words that could have told you, anyway — except perhaps those in a song that came out in the autumn of the following year — our last autumn together.

"Annie's Song," it was called, appropriately enough. When I heard it, I felt the young American singer had written it specially for us, for you and me, Annie, and so I bought it for you one Friday evening on

Continued on page 170. **167**

HE HEARS BUT DOES HE LISTEN?

There are times when I can get my husband to agree to anything — as long as I pick my moment very carefully.

By RONI BORDEN

MY husband's hearing is definitely programmed. There are some things that he always hears perfectly, even though he may be in another room.

"I can't go anywhere until I get our joint account balanced," I whispered to a friend on the phone, making certain that my husband was out of sight.

"If I don't get the account straightened out as soon as possible, I think the bank will be asking me for a divorce."

"What's this about our account?" my husband asked as he walked into the room.

On the other hand, I could be standing right next to him without him ever hearing a word.

"We haven't visited my mother in a long time and she asked if we'd like to spend next weekend with her," I said to my husband at breakfast.

"I hope I've managed to fix the car and that she's OK to start this morning," he answered as he left the table.

Certain activities have a definite, noticeable effect on his ability to hear — like when I think he's going to repair a leaky washer on the tap.

"Did I hear you say the kids need a lift to the library now?" he calls, slipping away.

While he is doing his income tax return he can pick up sounds, even from the cellar.

"The boiler is making a funny noise and if I don't have a look at it now we might not have any hot water tonight."

When he's watching someone else's holiday slides his hearing becomes so sharp he can identify sounds from as far away as the house next door.

168

"I thought I heard a car pull up to our house. Maybe I'd better check."

But there are exceptions to his hearing successes.

Any football match on television drowns out all sounds from the outside world.

The morning newspaper, which he reads at breakfast, makes him go totally deaf.

A discussion about the next election makes the rest of the world disappear.

WHILE it is true that my husband's hearing problems can be very frustrating at times, it is also true that, handled properly, the situation can be very helpful indeed.

"I've given away that old tatty jacket of yours for the jumble sale," I said to my husband one morning while he read the paper. "I hope that's all right with you."

"Uh-huh," came the placid reply.

"Fran and I decided that, for a change, we'd like to play golf with you and Mark instead of having the two of you go off by yourselves," I said during a Test match. "So we'll be going with you next Saturday."

"That's nice," my husband agreed.

But my most notable achievement to date took place about two months ago.

It was very successful.

"If you're planning to shower and change before we go out, we'd better eat dinner in a hurry," I said to my husband as soon as he came home from work.

"Shower and change?" my husband said, highly indignant. "Why do I have to shower and change to watch TV in my own living-room?"

"Don't you remember?" I said. "I reminded you this morning while you were having breakfast."

My husband never admits that he doesn't always hear everything I say, so he agreed.

"Of course I heard you, but I must have forgotten. What was it again?"

"We're going to the ballet tonight," I explained patiently. "The ballet company is on tour and this is a great chance to go and see them."

"Ballet!" My husband groaned. "You know how bored I get watching ballet. Why didn't you ask me before you went out and bought the tickets?"

"I did," I said righteously. "Remember? I asked about it while you and Andy were having that discussion about the candidates for the local elections."

So we went to the ballet.

But two can play at this game, so unless I'm very careful, I have a feeling that one of these days I could find myself spending a long day out fishing!

But I confess — the ballet was worth it. □

TO HAVE AND TO HOLD

Continued from page 167.

my way home from work.

Let me drown in your laughter. Let me die in your arms.

At times I felt I could ask nothing more of life than to do just that, Annie. To love you, and to die in your arms.

But instead it was you who died in mine, slipping into that other world while I held you and cried and begged you not to leave me.

We didn't have to take that train. That's what tortured me for so long afterwards.

We could have driven down to my sister's that winter day seven years ago, but it was such a boring journey on the motorway and it seemed easier to go by rail.

The story was in all the papers, of course. A miracle, they called it. Hundreds of people could have been killed when those two trains ploughed into each other.

Instead there were only five, so the media gave thanks and rejoiced.

But not me, Annie, not me, or the families of those other four people who had died in that crash.

For us there was no miracle. Just pain and anguish and that often repeated question, *Why?*

I CAN'T remember much about those first years after you left me — perhaps because we only remember the good times, and there is nothing good to remember.

Day followed day with a terrible numbing sameness, while I worked frenziedly in the office as if that could blot out all thought . . .

. . . And night piled upon night, proving that it was not so, raking up every one of those crushed hopes, each shattered dream.

Gradually, though, things got better. Few of us can mourn for ever.

"He's getting over it, thank God," I overheard one of my colleagues say after a couple of years had gone by.

And I suppose in a way it was true.

Granted, I didn't wake up at night calling for you and clutching at an empty pillow.

I didn't sit staring at the wall for hours on end, seeing your face before me.

Sometimes I even went for a drink with the boys and laughed at their jokes.

But is it possible to love someone so utterly and yet get over it in that time?

There were still songs I couldn't listen to, because I would remember you humming them.

Although it didn't hurt anymore to think of you, occasionally at a sad book or film, a lump would come in my throat that had really nothing to do with these make-believe events.

And then there was the odd, irrational fondness I would feel for complete strangers because something about them — just the way they walked, maybe, or the colour of their hair — reminded me of you.

THAT'S why what happened early last year was so unexpected. Because Susan isn't a bit like you, Annie.

She is taller, and perhaps a little heavier, too. Where your hair was fair and hung to your shoulders, Susan's hair is short, curly and dark.

In temperament, too, she is unlike you, her quiet gentleness a contrast to your bubbling enthusiasm and joy.

I don't know when exactly it was that I realised I loved her.

It wasn't a sudden thing. There were no flashing lights, no stars in my eyes, or abrupt blinding knowledge.

Instead it happened slowly, over a long period of time, during which she became more and more necessary in my life.

And now I want to marry her, Annie . . .

The park is getting more crowded now, but it's quieter over here away from the pond.

Sunlight filters through the trees, sprinkling the rough grass with the patches of light and shade that you always thought so beautiful.

You seem very close here, my darling. For a moment I could almost believe I had travelled back all those years in time.

Almost, but not quite, because that young man has gone, Annie, as you have gone. Perhaps he even went with you, leaving another, different Neil Harris in his place, one who is older, greying a little, and showing all those signs of age that will never mar your loveliness.

Help me, Annie. I don't know what to do.

Yet even as I say the words, I know it's not really true. I *do* know. I've known for over a week now, a week of sleepless nights, and guilt and misery.

It's not your help I want, Annie. It's your understanding and your blessing.

And I think perhaps I have found these things this morning, here in this place we loved, beside the old tree stump where I scratched our initials.

It looks different now, that tree. Someone has planted a honey-suckle and it has almost covered the old wood, so that our initials are no longer visible.

No casual eyes will glance at them now. No schoolchildren will laugh at the romantic nonsense of years ago. No other lovers will stop and wonder for a moment about "A.R." and "N.H.", then wander off and forget.

But they'll still be there, Annie. And, in summer, covered over by that fragrant blossom, buried in sweetness.

And I know that is the way you would have wanted it. □

Dream Of

The reality of a holiday is never quite the same as the dream. But sometimes — just sometimes — it's even better.